The NewAstro™

Zone System
for Astro Imaging

by Ron Wodaski

with additional material by Russell Croman

Everything you need to know

for processing CCD and Digital Camera images

with Photoshop® CS/CS2

NEW ASTRONOMY PRESS

Table of Contents

Published by New Astronomy Press
PO Box 6240, Kent WA 98064 USA

New Astronomy Press
http://www.newastro.com

Dedicated to my wife, Donna Brown,
who makes all things wonderful.

First Published 2006
Published in the United States of America
Printed by CDS Publications
Typeset in Adobe Garamond Pro and Myriad Pro
Layout by Chanel Clayton, New Astronomy Press

ISBN: 0-9711237-5-6

Printing: 10 9 8 7 6 5 4 3 2 1

The Zone System

The Zone System for Astro Imaging

Overview

Every image can be broken down into multiple zones. By applying the appropriate type of processing to each zone, you can bring out the best in any image.

- Zones allow you to apply the scientific method to image processing. They quantify what makes a good image.
- Zones break the image into manageable chunks. You don't have to figure out all the processing at once; you can do it step by step.
- Zones allow you to make sense out of histogram adjustments. Instead of guessing, you can follow a simple set of guidelines. You can control zones individually, and balance histogram adjustments between zones.
- The bottom line: identify the zones, and then apply the right processing to the right zone.

Details

There are four zones: Dark, Dim, Middle, and Bright. **Each zone is defined by the noise level in that zone.**

Dark Zone   The noise is extreme. In fact, there is so much noise that the only thing you can do with the Dark Zone is eliminate it from the image.

Dim Zone   There is significant noise, but with careful processing, you can preserve the details in the Dim Zone.

Middle Zone   Noise is moderate.

Bright Zone   Noise is minimal.

The lower the noise level in any part of the image, the more sharpening you can perform. The higher the noise level, the more you need things like smoothing.

The ultimate goal is to take lots of long exposures to put as much of the image into the Bright Zone as possible.

Definitions

Black point: Sets the darkest value in the image—all darker values will be rendered black.

Graininess: The visual appearance of noise in an image. The grain results from random variations in brightness levels—that is, noise. Grain is more obvious in dim areas.

Histogram: A graph that shows the relative number of pixels at each brightness value. The greater the number of pixels at a given brightness level, the higher the peak. Linear and non-linear changes affect the histogram.

Image Calibration (Reduction): Removing system noise from raw images. This typically includes applying dark frames, bias frames, and/or flat-field frames to an image.

Noise: Noise is the random uncertainty in brightness values. It's easy to misunderstand noise. Noise isn't something you can easily wrap your thoughts around—as often as not, metaphors will wind up taking you down the wrong road. Noise is a statistical phenomenon, and common sense and statistics do not line up for most of us. Getting a working grasp on what noise is, and what it means for your image processing, will be very helpful in taking your processing to the next level.

Read noise: The number of electrons in each pixel cannot be counted exactly for a variety of reasons. The random variations in brightness levels that results are called read noise.

Sharpening: Image processing technique that emphasizes details. The two dominant types of sharpening are Unsharp Masking and Deconvolution. Unsharp Masking blurs the image and then subtracts the blur, leaving a sharper image. Deconvolution is a mathematical filter that attempts to remove blurring introduced by seeing, optics, and other effects.

Shot noise: Also called Photon noise. These are the random variations in the arriving photons due to quantum effects. Mathematically, the shot noise is equal to the square root of the photon signal.

Signal to Noise ratio: (S/N) The signal level divided by the noise level. Since it is difficult to measure noise, this is more often used in a general way rather than a technical way. Dim areas have low signal relative to noise, so they have low S/N. Bright areas have high signal and a relatively lower noise level, so they have high S/N. High S/N is good, and allows more extensive processing on an image.

Smoothing: Smoothing is applied to the Dim Zone (and the darker portions of the Middle Zone) to reduce the visual impact of noise. Gaussian Blur (and Reduce Noise, Photoshop® CS2 only) are the most commonly used smoothing methods.

System noise: As if the whole idea of noise weren't intimidating enough, there are two types of noise commonly encountered in CCD image: true (or random) noise, and system noise. System noise is repeatable so it can be measured. This means you can remove it from an image. Random noise cannot be measured and removed, but it can be minimized. And here's an interesting point discussed in detail in this chapter: system noise itself has some random noise as well.

White point: Sets the brightest value in the image—all brighter values will be rendered white.

The Zones Revealed

The images below show how you can visualize the zones in an image. This is NGC 1491, an HII region imaged through a Hydrogen Alpha filter. The image at left shows the processed result using the Zone System. The image at right has been altered to show where the zones are located.

The proportion of the image in each zone depends on the length of exposure, and the total number of exposures. NGC 1491 is a dim object, so there is very little Bright Zone in the final image.

As is often the case, the Middle Zone dominates the image. Objects like the Lagoon Nebula, which has a large, broad area of bright nebulosity, will have a larger Bright Zone. Most objects are not as bright throughout, and they will have more Middle Zone than any other zone.

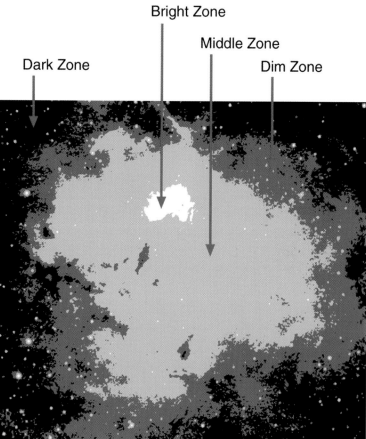

Dark Zone   Bright Zone   Middle Zone   Dim Zone

Signal to Noise Ratio

Zones are based on the signal to noise ratio in different parts of the image. A dim portion of the image has very little signal, while a bright area has a lot of signal.

The signal to noise ratio (abbreviated S/N), like any ratio, is simply one number divided by another. For example, if the signal is 1,000 and the noise is 25, then the S/N is simply 1,000 divided by 25 (1,000/25). To express this as a ratio, convention dictates that we use the colon, like this:

1,000:25

Further, convention tells us to make one side of the ratio expression unity (one). This is accomplished by dividing both sides of the expression by the lower number, 25 in this case. The result looks like this:

40:1

If the noise level were 25 across the image, then a bright area with a high signal (brightness level) of 30,000 will have a S/N of 1,200:1. A dim area with a low signal of 200 will have a S/N of 8:1.

Noise is not in fact constant across the image, and I will explain why a little later in this chapter (in the section Noise: Heart of the Zone System). Even so, the concept I want you to get is this: bright areas have high S/N, and dim areas have low S/N. This is important because:

- Areas with high S/N can be sharpened
- Areas with low S/N need smoothing

High S/N areas are typically things like galaxy cores, bright nebulosity, and of course longer exposures create better S/N values throughout the image.

Low S/N areas include such things as the image background, dim nebulosity, and the outer areas of a galaxy.

As you might have guessed, there is a very simple way to tell where the best S/N is in an image. The bright areas have the best S/N (as long as they are not saturated, of course).

For reasons explained later on, it is not simple to measure the amount of noise in an image. There are ways to estimate it, but fortunately there is a simple, trivial way to figure out where the best S/N is: brightness. That is why we use brightness to identify the zones in an image.

Different objects in an image can have different S/N ratios. For example, a widefield image of M81 and M82 includes galaxies with very different brightness levels. M82 is very bright and it is going to have the best S/N in the image. All but the core of M81 is much dimmer. You could easily wind up with each galaxy in a separate zone.

It's All About the Noise

Even though you can learn to estimate noise levels using brightness cues (and graininess helps, too), it's still important to understand what noise is and how it affects what you can do during image processing. I've included a complete section in this chapter that dives right into the facts about noise. Before we get technical, however, a little overview should help you get oriented.

Noise is something that most people would say they understand. This might be true when talking about, for example, the background noise at a party. But this is typically not true when we start looking closely at the mathematical realities of noise.

This might be easier to understand if we substitute new words for signal and noise. Try this:

Signal = Certainty

Noise = Uncertainty

In other words, instead of S/N, think in terms of:

Certainty/Uncertainty

Or, to put it in simplest terms:

Reality/Who Knows What

What does uncertainty (noise) do to an image? It makes the brightness values in the image variable. Suppose the variations are 25 brightness levels. Any brightness difference smaller than 25 brightness levels will be invisible in the image.

This uncertainty limits your processing choices. You can't sharpen an image to reveal details whose brightness difference is smaller than the noise level. (In fact, brightness details must be several times greater than the noise level to be visible.)

Uncertainty limits your processing choices. You would be wise to do anything you can to increase signal (certainty) and decrease noise (uncertainty) as you image and then process those images. S/N dictates your processing choices.

The image of M51 above has extremely low S/N, which means that brightness levels have large variability. So large, in fact, that even the spiral arms are barely discernible. This is one of my own very early images, and is just a few seconds of exposure time.

The image above, on the other hand, has superb S/N and reveals not only the presence of spiral arms, but an enormous amount of details within those arms.

Better S/N yields more certainty in the image, and it opens up processing options that will transform what you can do with your images.

Histogram Zones

The figure at right shows how zones relate to the image histogram. Low S/N is found at the left side of the histogram, where the black point resides. High S/N is found at the right side of the histogram, where the white point resides.

The pseudo white point is marked; it is used for color balancing. It is not the same as the image white point. See chapter 6 for information on color balancing.

The Dark Zone is the space at the left of the main peak in the histogram. The Dim Zone is the left half of the peak. The Middle Zone occupies the rest of the peak, and the Bright Zone is the rest of the histogram out of the right edge. The exact balance between the zones will depend on the overall noise level (and thus on the total exposure time of the combined image).

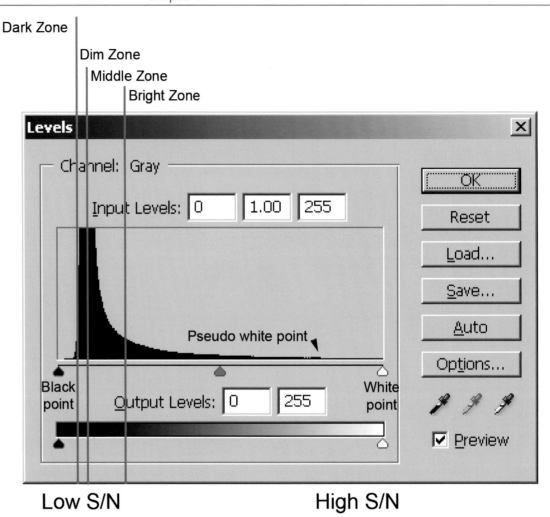

The images on the facing page show what you can do with the Zone System to control the appearance of an image.

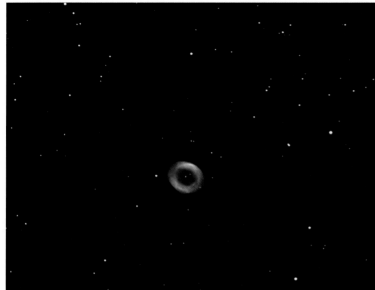

Zone System Example: Ring Nebula

The image at top left has only a standard contrast stretch (called background/range or min/max). The Ring Nebula is OK, but dim details are completely lost. The image at bottom left uses Digital Development defaults in MaxIm DL. The background details show up a little bit, but the ring doesn't have adequate contrast to reveal structure.

The image at bottom right uses custom settings for Digital Development. Ring contrast is OK, but dim details are lost.

The image on the following page uses the Zone System. Dim background details are vividly displayed (check out the background galaxies and the Ring's outer shell), and the contrast of the Ring Nebula is also preserved.

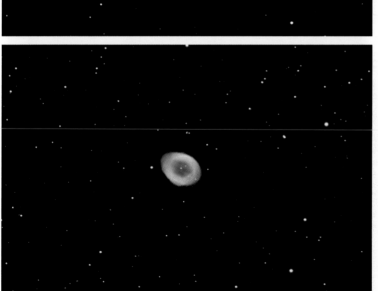

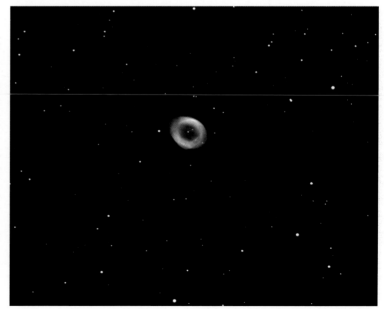

The image below shows what can be done using the Zone System to process an image. Compare this result to the automated and customized processing examples on the previous page. The Zone System gives you much more control.

You can control individual zones and balance contrast between zones. In addition, you can separate sharpening from contrast changes. Overall, the Zone System gives you the best results possible for almost any image.

Noise: Heart of the Zone System

If you understand what noise is, and how it affects your images, you have the keys to the Zone System.

Noise isn't so much a thing as a concept. In fact, preconceptions about noise can easily get in the way of getting a good grasp of the Zone System. Let's start at the very beginning, and build up a useful understanding of noise from scratch.

Engrave this somewhere in your memory banks:

Noise is the uncertainty in the data.

That's right—noise isn't a thing, nor is it easily measurable. Noise consists of random variations in the brightness levels of an image. For example, suppose that we image a blank wall that has a true brightness value of 100. Suppose further that we have some simple device that allows us to take measurements of the brightness of that wall. Noise will result in values that cluster around the true value—98, 95, 102, 110, 93, and so on. The variations are random, and no one measurement will give us the true value of the brightness of the wall. Each measurement will vary from the truth by some amount. These variations are noise.

Where does the noise come from in a CCD image? It comes from a variety of sources. The most significant sources are **read noise** and **shot noise**. (More about these in a moment.)

A CCD chip works by converting incoming photons into electrons. At the end of an exposure, the electrons in each pixel are counted, and sent to your computer.

Read noise occurs when the CCD chip doesn't count the number of electrons accurately. Electrons are counted in a special pixel on the CCD chip. Some electrons might "stick" to the pixel and not get read. Some electrons might sneak in during the counting process. By whatever means, read noise results in random variations from pixel to pixel as the data is being read from the chip.

The amount of read noise is the number of electrons by which the read operation can vary from the true value. This does not mean that the read operation will be off by that value every time. If the read noise is, say, ±10 electrons at 0° C, then for each pixel the uncertainty (noise) will be a total of 20 electrons. Any given pixel might be off by zero, −5, 9, etc.

Note the presence of a temperature in that description. The colder a CCD chip is, the lower the overall noise will be. This is why most CCD chips in astronomical cameras are cooled.

Shot noise, also called photon noise, results from the quantum nature of light. In other words, light itself is noisy. Shot noise follows a very simple rule: the noise (uncertainty) is equal to the square root of the signal. So if the brightness level is 100, the shot noise is 10.

Noise Control

An analysis of the two types of noise demonstrates a key fact. The uncertainty of the read operation is the same no matter how bright the image is. That is, a longer exposure has the same read noise as a short exposure. However, the uncertainty of the shot noise increases with exposure time. (Fortunately, the signal increases at a faster rate than the noise. The S/N of shot noise always gets better with longer exposures.)

This leads to a simple strategy for controlling noise. If the exposure is long enough, the shot noise will dominate, nearly eliminating read noise as a factor. In other words, the total noise in the image will be nearly equal to the square root of the signal level. (If read noise is 10, and shot noise is 1,000, then the read noise is only 1% of the total noise. It becomes a non-factor.)

Because different CCD chips have different levels of read noise, there isn't a single exposure time that will yield a shot noise high enough to obscure the read noise. In addition, the brightness of the sky plays a large role in the shot noise. The brighter your sky, the more rapidly the shot noise will cover the read noise. This sounds good, but think of the penalty here: a brighter sky is a noisier sky. That is why dark skies are so desirable for astronomical imaging.

Shot noise from background brightness will be lower at a dark-sky site, but the contribution of read noise will be proportionally higher. So longer exposures are the norm for dark sites, and shorter exposures for bright sites.

The goal then is an exposure long enough to swamp the read noise with the shot noise. That exposure length depends on the shot noise at your imaging location.

The most useful way to determine the minimum exposure time is with the image background brightness. For a given sensor and location, a certain exposure length optimizes the read noise/shot noise ratio.

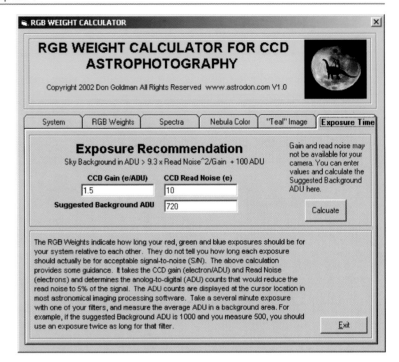

Stan Moore has web pages dedicated to calculating the optimal background level:

http://home.earthlink.net/~stanleymm/CCD_topics.html

Don Goldman's RGB Weight Calculator includes Stan's calculations (see above) along with other very useful tools:

http://www.astrodon.com

CCDWare has a web page dedicated to determining the optimum exposure time for your site:

http://www.ccdware.com/resources/subexposure.cfm

The Dark Zone

The Dark Zone is that portion of the image that is so dominated by noise that it is useless for presentation in the final image.

Put in simplest terms, the Dark Zone is the lost portion of the image. It's a throwaway. Use the black point to get rid of the Dark Zone completely. By raising the black point until the Dark Zone is hidden, you will dramatically improve the appearance of an image.

The image at left below shows what lurks in the Dark Zone: horrendous noise. There is horizontal streaking from excessive read noise, and there is lots of random noise as well. The exact nature of the noise you'll find in the Dark Zone will vary from one camera to the next, but the overall result will be similar to what you see here. That's why the Dark Zone has

to go. Raising the black point takes care of the problem, as shown at lower right.

You won't always be able to simply raise the black point to the precise correct level in one try. If the exposure time is short, it is easy to go too far with the black point. I usually work on the black point several times while processing an image, getting it closer to the ideal point as the image processing reveals more of the dim details in the image.

You should use the image histogram to guide you in placing the black point, as shown in chapter 2, ***Photoshop® Basics: The Standard Curve.***

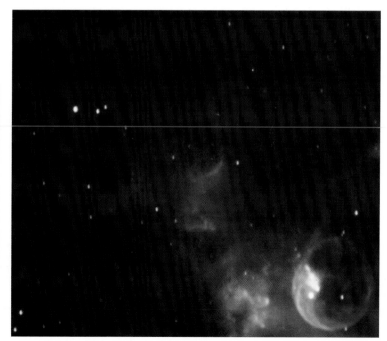

Noise is present throughout an image, but it shows up most clearly in the Dark Zone because there is little signal in the Dark Zone. In other words, the signal to noise ratio (S/N) is very poor in the Dark Zone.

Anything you do to reduce noise will push the Dark Zone down further, giving you more dim details in your images.

☙ Tip: Longer exposure times push areas of the image up the zone scale. Dim moves to Middle, Middle moves to Bright.

Here are some techniques that will lower your noise levels:

• Long total exposure time. Think in terms of hours, not minutes.

• Long enough individual exposures to minimize the contribution of read noise. See earlier sections of this chapter for web links for determining this exposure time.

• Dark skies. Not much you can do about this when you image from the typical back yard, but if you can get out to a dark site you'll see significant benefits.

• Sharp focus. Even a slight mis-focus will spread out the light and reduce contrast and detail in the image. This reduces the signal level, and makes noise more prominent. Yes, that means you can attack the noise problem in two ways: by reducing noise, and increasing signal.

• Careful image calibration/reduction, using large numbers of bias, dark and flat fields. See chapter 4 for more information about calibration and reduction.

Why Is Noise Grainy?

The above question illustrates a common misconception about noise. You probably think about noise like this: "The noisiest parts of the image are obvious because they show the most grain." This is not correct because the noise level in the image is constant. It is the signal level that changes across the image. The correct description is: "The most signal-deprived areas of the image are obvious because they show the most grain."

For example, assume that the noise level is 10. Let's compare two areas of the image with different signal levels. One area has a signal level of 100, with a signal to noise ratio (S/N) of 10:1. The other area has a signal level of 1,000 for a S/N of 100:1.

In the area with S/N of 10:1, the individual pixels vary by up to 10% of the signal level. It is easy to see this level of individual variation because the random variations in pixel brightness are a significant percentage of the signal level. Low S/N is typical of the Dark and Dim zones of an image, and the large relative differences from pixel to pixel make these zones look grainy.

In the area with S/N of 100:1, the individual pixels vary by no more than 1% of the signal level. The eye can't distinguish such small variations, and the area appears much less noisy, perhaps even noise free. The random variations are such a small percentage of the signal level that the eye can't see the differences very well.

The Dim Zone

The Dim Zone is the noisy but salvageable portion of the image.

The Dim Zone is noisy, but not so noisy that it needs to be gotten rid of. With a little smoothing and blurring, the Dim Zone can be made to look quite respectable.

Despite the presence of noise in the Dim Zone, the eye can perceive at least some details. The details are typically obscured by noise. Details that have strong enough contrast to rise above the noise will be visible, but more subtle details, with minimal contrast, do not rise above the noise levels.

The irony with the Dim Zone is that in many images it contains the most interesting information. Dim nebulosity, the outer areas of galaxies—all of these are full of interesting details. Long exposures will bring out the most in the dim areas, but careful Dim Zone processing will reveal as much detail as is present in the data. Without proper Dim Zone processing, details might get lost and never be revealed.

This leads to a simple fact that has led many an image processor to frustration: the Dim Zone is the hardest zone to process, yet it contains the most desired details. Careful application of smoothing, followed by careful Zone System processing, will save the day.

The figures above are details from a larger image (see next page) that show before and after processing for the Dim Zone. The top image is the raw original. The bottom image shows the appearance of this area after smoothing. See chapter 3 for details on applying smoothing to the Dim Zone of an image.

The image of NGC 5566 above is a raw image without smoothing. The lower right corner of the box was used for the smoothing example on the previous page. Most of the area included in the box is part of the image's Dim Zone.

The Middle Zone

The portion of the image between the Dim and Bright Zones.

The above definition seems like a cop-out, but there just isn't a better one available. The Dim Zone is well defined by dominant noise; the Bright Zone is well defined by extremely low noise. The Middle Zone is simply the stuff between those two extremes.

In fact, you can make a good case for a continuum including the Dim, Middle, and Bright Zone. The boundaries between Dim/Middle and Middle/Bright are fuzzy at best. The darker portion of the Middle Zone needs some of the same processing as the Dim Zone, just less of it. Likewise, the lighter portions of the Middle Zone can use a bit of the same type of processing as the Bright Zone.

In a sense, you could say that the Middle Zone can be divided into three sub-zones: Dim–Middle, Middle–Middle, and Bright–Middle. As you gain more skill with processing using Zones, such distinctions allow you to fine-tune your techniques.

The bottom line for the Middle Zone is that it's not noisy enough to need much smoothing, and S/N isn't good enough to encourage sharpening. The bulk of the processing for the Middle Zone is the histogram changes that are used to bring out dim details. See chapter 2, **Photoshop® Basics: The Standard Curve,** for an example of histogram processing.

The above example shows an extreme case of an image that consists only of Dim and Middle Zones. This is a small portion of the Pelican Nebula. Consisting of a single exposure, it just doesn't have a Bright Zone. (To be technically correct, it does have a Bright Zone—the stars. But what we really want is to have some of the nebula in the Bright Zone!) Smoothing salvaged the image, and even though it's somewhat dark, it's still an interesting result.

The Bright Zone

The Bright Zone contains the areas of the image with the best signal to noise ratio.

The Bright Zone is the easiest portion of the image to work with. Noise is extremely low compared to the signal, and you typically can't even detect the noise at all, at least not visually.

The Bright Zone is your prime area for sharpening, but you'll need to be careful not to overdo it. The right amount of sharpening will reveal details that were hidden prior to sharpening. If you over-sharpen, however, you'll create artifacts instead of revealing details. Keep an eye on the image, and use your knowledge of the object, to determine how much sharpening to use. The stronger the signal in the Bright Zone, the less likely you are to generate artifacts.

The two most common sharpening methods are deconvolution and unsharp masking. Photoshop® does not include deconvolution tools, but most CCD control programs include one or more deconvolution methods. These include MaxIm DL, CCDSoft, CCDSharp, Astroart, and many others. The exact features vary from version to version, however.

Many of these programs also include good tools for unsharp masking. Photoshop® supports unsharp masking as well, and you'll find some useful and innovative advice in chapter 3.

NOTE: Each type of sharpening has characteristic types of artifacts that you'll need to watch out for, and this is covered in the various chapters on sharpening.

You can also use unsharp masking outside of the Bright Zone using large-feature sharpening (also covered in chapter 3). Normally, the noise in the Middle and Dim Zones results in excessive artifacts rather than useful sharpening. By raising the Threshold setting, you can apply sharpening safely to zones that normally would not benefit from sharpening.

The ideal image would have lots of area in the Bright Zone. There is a very simple rule you can follow to put as much of the image as possible into the Bright Zone:

You can increase the portion of the image in the Bright Zone by using a longer total exposure time.

That sounds simple, and it is simple. The longer you expose, the easier your image will be to process. When I am teaching classes on image processing, students frequently ask me what is the one thing they can do to improve their image processing. My answer: take longer exposures. The Dim Zone is the toughest part of the image to process. The Middle Zone is better, and the Bright Zone is practically a slam dunk. By taking longer exposures, you solve most of the image processing problems before you even start your processing.

Even an object with very little bright content benefits from longer total exposure time. Moving parts of the image from the Dim Zone to the Middle Zone is worthwhile because you will often image objects that just don't have that much brightness to start with. It is *relative* brightness, not absolute brightness, that determines the zones!

The figures on the facing page show the value of combining multiple exposures to get a long total exposure time.

Single Image

Combined Images

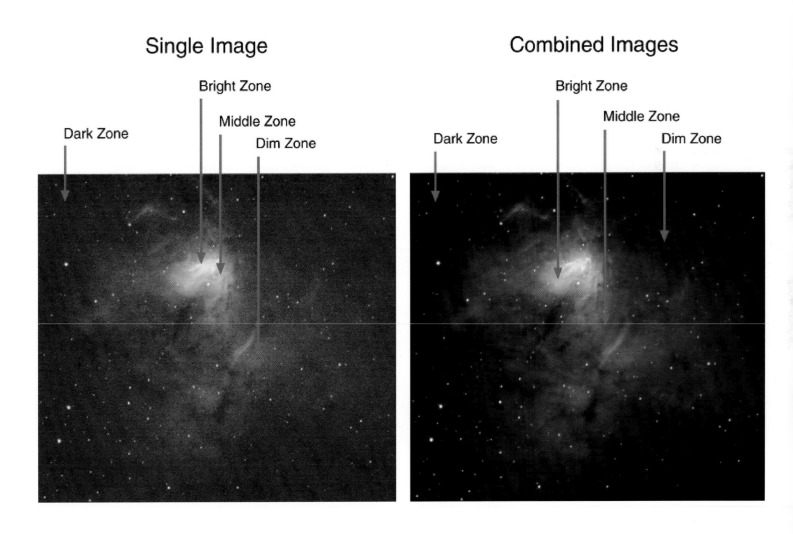

Bright Zone

Middle Zone

Dim Zone

Dark Zone

Bright Zone

Middle Zone

Dim Zone

Dark Zone

The Lagoon Nebula is a very bright object, and this image contains mostly Bright Zone material. Sharpening has brought out numerous details in the image.

Note how sharpening the Bright Zone also emphasized dim details. Sharpening often enhances the boundary between bright and dim regions.

Review

Noise is inevitable when taking CCD images. By learning how noise affects different zones, you can apply the right processing tricks to the right zones and get the best results.

Keys to success:

- Noise is the bane of CCD imaging. By controlling random noise sources (read noise, shot noise) you can optimize and minimize your noise levels. Further, by diligent removal of system noise, you can clean up your images to the greatest extent possible.

- Read noise is more or less constant in an image. Long individual exposures limit the contribution of read noise to an individual image.

- Shot noise changes with the signal. It is equal to the square root of the signal, so it grows more slowly than signal. Long total exposure time limits the contribution of shot noise.

- It's important to understand noise, but the real issue is the ratio of signal to noise (S/N). The better your signal to noise overall, the more freedom you have to process the image, and the more details you can reveal.

- Different areas of the image have different S/N. This applies no matter how much signal you have overall—the brighter parts of the image will always have the best S/N. With longer exposures, more of the image will have good enough S/N to be in the Bright Zone. But the actual S/N will always be better for the brighter parts of the image.

- Noise is primarily a problem in the Dark and Dim Zones of an image. This isn't because such areas have more noise; it's because they have less signal. The longer your total exposure time, the smaller the area of your image that will be in the Dark and Dim Zones.

- The four zones are: Dark (heavy noise, throw it away); Dim (noisy, but salvageable with smoothing); Middle (moderate noise, minimal processing); Bright (low noise, enhance with sharpening).

- To control noise in the Dim Zone, apply some smoothing. The most common smoothing tool is the Gaussian blur.

- To bring out details in the Bright Zone, apply some sharpening with deconvolution or unsharp masking.

- Sharpening brings the risk of creating artifacts instead of revealing details. Experiment to find out how much sharpening you can do on a given image without creating artifacts.

This image of M95 shows good zone control. The noise of the Dark and Dim Zones is not evident because the black point has been set appropriately. The details in the Bright Zone are clearly and carefully revealed. In particular, the details in the unusual core of the galaxy are visible. The Middle Zone details are not sharpened very much, but they are clear and show little evidence of noise.

Photoshop® Basics:
The Standard Curve

Photoshop® Basics: The Standard Curve

Objective

Bring out the dim details in an image, while preserving bright details effectively.

Techniques
- Set white point
- Set black point
- Linear and non-linear histogram stretching

Tools
- Photoshop® Levels
- Photoshop® Curves

Description

This chapter covers the heart and soul of image processing for just about any astronomical image. You will learn how to apply the principles of the Zone System using Photoshop® CS (or later). Other image processing programs, such as Picture Window Pro and Paint Shop Pro, include similar tools but the Levels and Curves tools in Photoshop® are powerful and fluid. Photoshop® CS adds a critically important feature: the ability to use layers and other tools with 16-bit images. Since 16-bit images contain up to 256 times as much information as 8-bit images, this is a very important feature for CCD image processing.

The key to success is mastering the somewhat challenging Curves dialog. You will learn the basic shape of a useful curve, as well as how to tweak that basic shape to get specific results. You will also learn how to use Curves to balance the available brightness levels between Zones.

Basic processing involves defining the range of data you want to work with (setting black and white points with Levels), and then expanding the dark areas and compressing the bright areas using Curves. Typically, you will use multiple iterations of Curves to accomplish your goals. You will use Levels several times to keep the black point appropriately controlled.

Definitions

Black point: A Levels slider for setting the darkest value in the image—all darker values will be rendered black. Used to remove the Dark Zone data from the image.

Clipping: Said of a Curve when it reaches the top line of the graph before reaching the right-hand side of the graph. Effectively lowers the white point, which is often undesirable. Clipping is usually avoided by adding additional points to the right of the existing point(s), and reshaping the Curve so it no longer clips.

Curves: A Photoshop® tool for making non-linear adjustments to the image's histogram. You add points to the curve to control which portions of the data are expanded or contracted. Expansion means that more of the available brightness levels are used for the data; contraction means that fewer brightness levels are used. When more brightness levels are allocated to a region, contrast is commonly said to be "stretched" (expanded is a more accurate term, however) in that region. Since there are a fixed number of brightness levels, if you stretch in one region, then you must contract in another. Typically, you expand in the dim areas, and contract in the brighter areas.

Gamma: A slider in the Levels tool that adjusts brightness and contrast simultaneously using a midpoint adjustment. Moving the slider to the left moves the midpoint to a dimmer portion of the image, allocating more brightness levels for the dim portions of the image, which brightens the image overall. See Curves—in a sense, Gamma is a simplified Curve tool.

Grayscale: A palette consisting only of gray values (no color). When you load a FITS image into Photoshop®, it is automatically assigned a Mode of Grayscale.

Histogram: A graph that shows the relative number of pixels at each brightness value. The greater the number of pixels at a given brightness level, the higher the peak. Linear and non-linear changes affect the histogram. You can use the histogram to evaluate how effectively Levels and Curves are modifying the data.

Levels: A Photoshop® tool for making linear adjustments to the image's histogram. See Curves for comparison. Levels is used to adjust the White Point and Black Point (and occasionally the Midpoint is moved for Gamma adjustments).

Linear: Brightness and Contrast adjustments that preserve the internal brightness relationships of the image. Nothing is expanded or contracted. Linear changes are typically limited to changing the White Point and Black Point.

Midpoint: Used to adjust image Gamma. See Gamma.

Non-linear: Brightness and Contrast adjustments that do not preserve internal brightness relationships. One part of the image may get a large boost, while another part may get only a small boost, or even a cut, in brightness and/or contrast.

Points: Added to the Curves dialog to control how much boost or cut each brightness range in the image receives.

White point: A Levels slider for setting the brightest value in the image—all brighter values will be rendered white. Lower the white point when there is no data in the brightest values.

Photoshop® Tips

The Levels and Curves dialogs are mainstays of Photoshop® processing. Both are found on the *Image»Adjustments* sub-menu.

Levels

The Levels dialog displays an image histogram. There are three sliders below the histogram that allow you to set the image's black point, midpoint, and white point.

Black point: The darkest brightness level in the image. All pixels darker than the black point will be rendered as black.

White point: The brightest level. All pixels brighter than the white point will be rendered as white.

Midpoint: Divides the image into two zones. The left side will be rendered with one half of the available levels, and the right side will be rendered with the other half. For example, if you move the midpoint slider to the left, the image will brighten because the darker values now occupy more than half of the available brightness levels.

The black point and white point settings are used often, but the midpoint setting is used infrequently. Curves is a more powerful way of solving the same types of problems. Use the midpoint slider for minor adjustments to make an image a little brighter or a little darker.

The midpoint slider adjusts image gamma. Gamma controls the brightness and contrast of an image simulta-neously. Gamma is not as powerful as Curves; it is a simpler approach to adjusting the image histogram.

NOTE: The brightness of your monitor controls how dark or bright your images appear. For best results, perform a monitor calibration using the tools provided with Photoshop®. You can use a third party tool such as Pantone's Spyder series of calibration tools. Or you can purchase a monitor that comes with its own calibration hardware, such as the Sony Artisan.

❧ TIP: The Levels dialog contains 256 brightness levels. Your CCD images typically have 65,536 brightness levels. This means that you must work at a lower resolution in the Levels dialog (and in Curves). That is why you repeat Levels and Curves multiple times: to increase the precision of your adjustments.

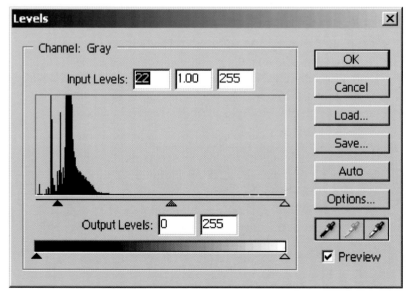

Curves

The Curves dialog is one of the richest, and most complex, areas of Photoshop®. This complexity gives you a lot of processing power, however, so the Curves dialog is worth some close study. You'll see many examples of different things you can do with Curves throughout the book.

The example at right shows a typical shape for a curve used with astronomical images. I call this the Standard Curve. You will find that you can use a curve like this for generalized brightening of your image, which will get it to the point where you can start to use the more advanced Zone System techniques. The important thing to note here is that you can have more than one point on a curve, and that Photoshop® automatically fits the curve to the points that you add.

The points correspond roughly to the zones in the image—that's what makes it a Standard Curve. Working from bottom left toward upper right, the four zones occupy the spaces between the points. Note that the first point is in the bottom left corner; it represents zero brightness and is the start of the Dark Zone. The next point (up and to the right) is approximately on the boundary between the Dark and Dim Zones.

⅍ TIP: You might wonder how I can say that these points correspond (approximately!) to the zones when the zones are relative. The answer is simple: this is only true if the black point has been correctly adjusted. Using Levels, always move the black point just to the left of the histogram peak.

NOTE: There are grayscale bars at left and bottom of the graph. If the darker portion of the bars is not at lower left,

click the double-headed arrow in the middle of the lower grayscale bar to flip the bars.

⅍ TIP: Click and drag the cursor in the image to see where on the curve a given brightness level lives.

⅍ TIP: To add a point on the curve that precisely matches a brightness level in the image, hold down the Control key and click in the image.

⅍ TIP: You can edit the numeric values of a point by changing the values in the Input and Output text boxes. To move to a point so you can edit it, use the Control + Tab keys.

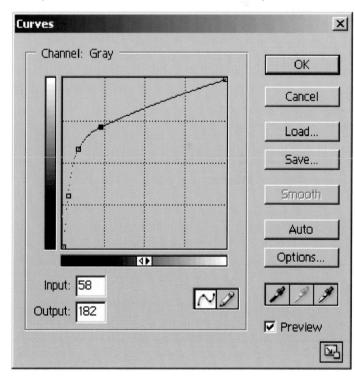

Processing Checklist

- ¤ Levels: Set the white point at the top of the histogram.

  Whether or not you need to set the white point depends on your camera and exposure duration. Some cameras have a saturation below a brightness level of 65,536; lower the white point to whatever the saturation value is. If your exposure is too short to reach saturation, you will also lower the white point to match.

- ¤ Levels: Set the black point just to the left of the data peak.

- ¤ Curves: Use the Standard Curve to expand dim data and compress bright data.

  The Standard Curve contains a point to brighten the Dim Zone; a point to establish the boundary between expansion and contraction (which takes the form of a turn on the curve somewhere in the Middle Zone); and if necessary a Control Point to yield a flat line to the top right corner. This last point helps eliminate clipping.

- ¤ Levels: Refine black point after every use of Curves. This eliminates the Dark Zone with increasing precision.

  Otherwise, you wind up expanding the Dark Zone, which is useless!

- ¤ Repeat last two steps until you just can see dimmest details (Dim Zone).

  It is important to stop before you brighten the Dim Zone too much. Otherwise, your options for adjusting all of the zones will be too limited. I would suggest you learn to stop a little bit short of actually being able to see the Dim Zone details. Use a temporary Curve to find the dimmest of the Dim Zone details, and then start over using the numeric value you determined.

- ¤ Curves: Determine numeric value of dimmest visible details (darkest part of Dim Zone). Use Control + Left Click to place a point on the curve matching this brightness level, or add it manually.

- ¤ Curves: Boost the dimmest visible details by raising the point on the curve as much as the noise allows.

  This establishes the brightness level of the Dim Zone. You might need to start over at this step if this gives too many brightness levels to the Dim data. Too many brightness levels dedicated to the Dim Zone leaves too few for the other zones.

- ¤ Curves: Balance the 256 available brightness levels between the remaining zones: Dim, Middle, and Bright. This is interzone contrast adjustment.

  This is where you typically deviate from the Standard Curve. Simply add a point for each zone you want to adjust (by Control Clicking on a point in the image that matches the zone), and then move them up or down to adjust brightness. You can move left and right to adjust contrast, or if your estimate of the zone location was wrong.

- ¤ Optional: If you have objects that have very different brightness levels, consider copying the objects to different layers so that you can use different Curves on each layer.

  Use full Zone System processing on each layer, ignoring the portions of the image away from the object. When the individual adjustments on each layer are complete, delete the undesired portions of each layer above the Background layer so you can "see" through the extra layers.

- ¤ Curves: Make micro-contrast adjustments to reveal structure in the image. These are intrazone adjustments.

- Color Range: Select the stars using Color Range and save the selection.

  First, duplicate the background layer and remove the stars from the duplicate using the Dust & Scratches filter. Then set the blend mode of the star-free layer to Difference. If done right, only the stars show through and you can select them with Color Range.

- Selection: Modify the selection by expanding it and feathering the edge. The amounts depend on the star diameters.

  You need some background around the star for effective processing.

- Layers palette: Duplicate via copy to create a stars layer.

  Right click on the layer name, and choose Duplicate via copy from the pop-up menu.

- Layers palette: If necessary, use Duplicate via cut to break the stars into groups with similar background brightness.

  Right click on the layer name, and choose Duplicate via cut. The idea here is to get stars with roughly equal background levels into the same layer so you can process them all at the same time.

- Curves: Use Stars curve to clean up stars.

  There is a standard curve for this, but it is very different from the Standard Curve. The key to success is to adjust the bottom left of the curve to make sure the bit of background around the stars matches the background in the layer below. Otherwise, you wind up with dark or bright halos around the stars because of the mismatch in brightness levels.

- Blend mode: If necessary, create a copy of the stars layer and then use the Darken blend mode and the Offset filter to clean up star elongation.

- Filters: Make the background image active in the Layers palette, and use Color Range and the Gaussian Blur to smooth the Dim Zone.

- Filters: Make the background image active in the Layers palette, and use selection tools and Unsharp Masking to sharpen the Bright Zone.

Running Man Nebula

Open a File

When you open a CCD image file in Photoshop, you often will not see much detail in the image. The brightest stars might be visible as shown here, or you might not see anything at all. This is normal! Most CCD images have 65,536 brightness levels, and only a small percentage of them are bright enough to be visible.

The easiest way to work with your CCD files in Photoshop is to use a FITS plug-in. (Most CCD files are stored in FITS format.)

There are free versions of FITS plug-ins available, as well as pay versions with specific features you might find helpful. The two most commonly used are the FITS Plug-in from Eddie Trimarchi, and FITS Liberator from NASA:

http://www.fitsplug.com

http://hubblesource.stsci.edu/sources/toolbox/entry/fits_liberator/

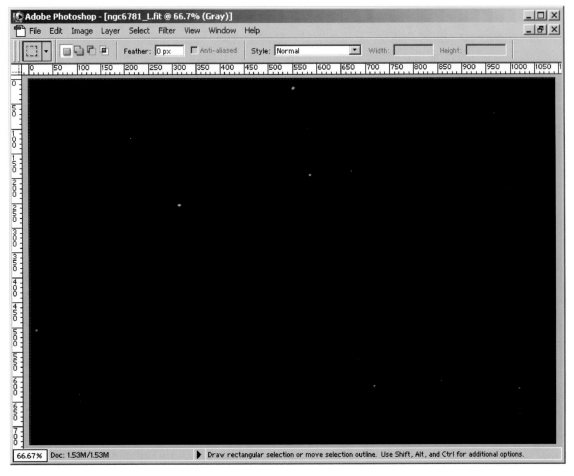

If you would like to follow along with this exercise, open the following file from the DVD in Photoshop® CS (or later):

\C2\m74_final.fit

Set the Black Point and White Point

To access the Levels dialog, use the *Image»Adjustments» Levels* menu item

The Levels dialog displays the image's histogram, a graph of the brightness values in an image. The histograms at right are more or less typical for astronomical images.

The left side of the histogram maps darker values, and the right side maps brighter values. Both histograms tell us that there are a large number of darker values (the peaks at far left), and very few bright values—there is just a dribble of values in the rest of the image in both examples.

The dribble of bright values completely runs out toward the right side of the histogram at top right. This means that there are no values brighter than where the thin black line stops. The white point needs to be set at this juncture, as shown at top right. Click and drag the open triangle (slider) until it is under the point where the data runs out.

In the bottom right example, there is open space to the left of the data peak. This means the black point needs to be raised. Move the black point slider just to the left of the start of the data peak, as shown. No adjustment to the white point is required for this file.

NOTE: Make the adjustment at lower right if you are following along with the exercise in Photoshop CS.

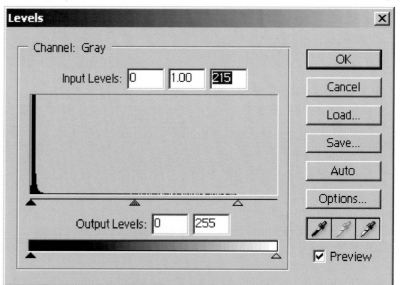

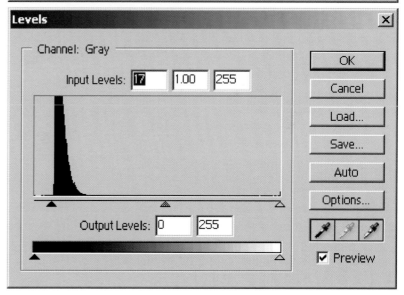

Curves Dialog

To access the Curves dialog, use the *Image » Adjustments » Curves* menu item.

The Curves dialog looks innocent at first glance. It's only when you use it that you realize how complex it is. Given that the Curves dialog is the single most powerful (and thus most commonly used) tool for astro imagers, a road map will help you find your way.

❧ TIP: Make sure that the grayscale bars at left and bottom of the Curves dialog are oriented as shown. If necessary, click the double-headed arrow located at the middle of the bottom grayscale bar to flip the orientation of the bars.

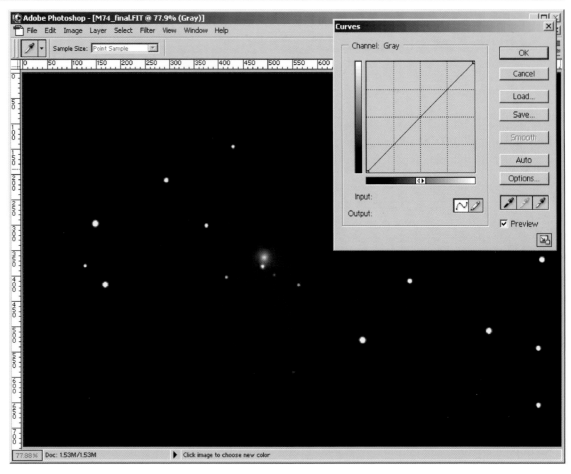

The diagonal line on the Curves graph is the heart and soul of this tool. The diagonal line represents zero change, and is always the starting condition. Your job is to turn that line into an appropriate curve, so I will call it a curve from now on—even when it is a straight line.

There are already two points on the curve: one at bottom left, and one at top right. These are the default points that define the curve. They correspond to the black and white points.

To make changes to the image, click on the curve to add one or more points, and then drag the point to reshape the curve.

Add a Point

The left side of the Curves graph controls the dim portions of the image, and the right side controls the bright portions. As you learn the Zone System, you can place points on the curve corresponding closely to the positions of the various zones—even sub-zones.

Click on the curve to add points. Click and drag to reposition a point. Photoshop adjusts the curve to include the new location of the point. Dragging up, as shown here, brightens the corresponding portion of the image. Dragging down darkens, and is seldom used.

In this example, the added point is on the left half of the Curves graph, so the dim

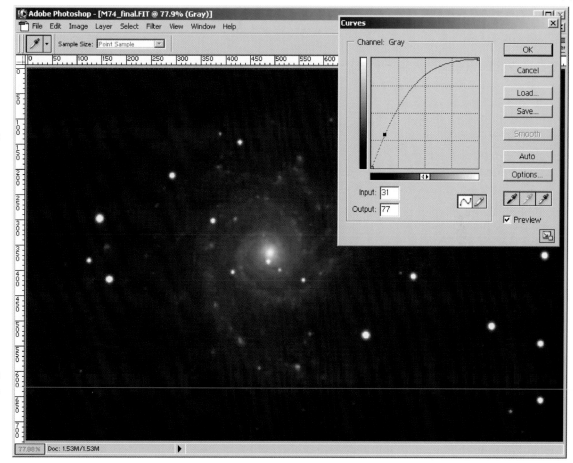

portions of the image are brightened. The curve adjusts to the added point, so bright portions of the image are also affected (You'll learn how to prevent unwanted changes to the bright portion of the image shortly. This is accomplished by adding additional points to the Curves graph.)

❧ TIP: Increasing the brightness of dim areas often makes the background brighter. Always use Levels to compensate by refining the position of the black point. It's almost always necessary to make Levels adjustments after changes to Curves.

Aggression

You can be more or less aggressive with how you add
points in the Curves dialog.
In the preceding example,
the point wasn't very aggressive. In this example, the
first point is very aggressive. The slope of the curve
tangent to the point is very
high. So high, in fact, that
the curve crunches into the
top of the graph. This is
called clipping, and it is not
a good thing.

NOTE: We will deal with
clipping shortly.

The effect of this aggressive first point is to greatly
enhance the visibility of the
dim portions of the image.
The outer arms of M74 are
bright and clear with this
point adjustment.

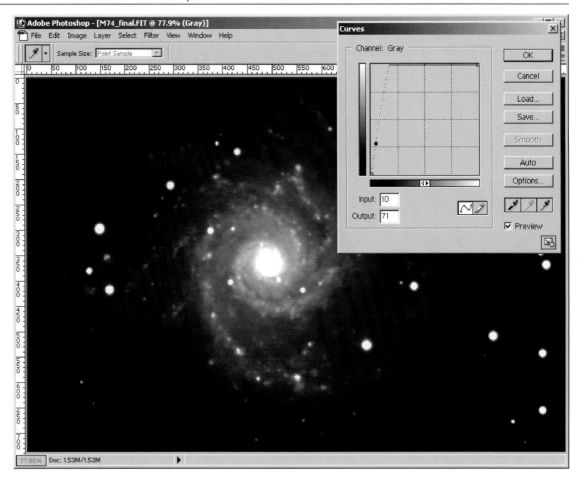

NOTE: You won't always see this much detail when you add
the first point, even with a very aggressive setting. That's OK,
because you can do more than one iteration of Curves. This
happens with short exposures, and with emission-line images.

The curve shown above has a positive impact on the Dim
Zone, but it's too aggressive for the Middle and Bright Zones.
We need a way to keep the positive changes in the Dim Zone,
but to prevent problems in the other zones.

Adding a Second Point

As shown at right, I have added a second point to the curve. This second point has a less aggressive slope than the first point. This is typical—we are building what I call the Standard Curve.

The first point dramatically enhanced the appearance of dim portions of the image, but it also pushed the bright areas of the image too hard. The core of the galaxy was washed out. This second point reduces the impact of the curve on the Middle and Bright Zones by lowering it.

This adjustment affects mostly the Middle Zone because the position of the point matches that zone. Despite the improvements, the Bright Zone at the core of the galaxy is still a problem—it is all white.

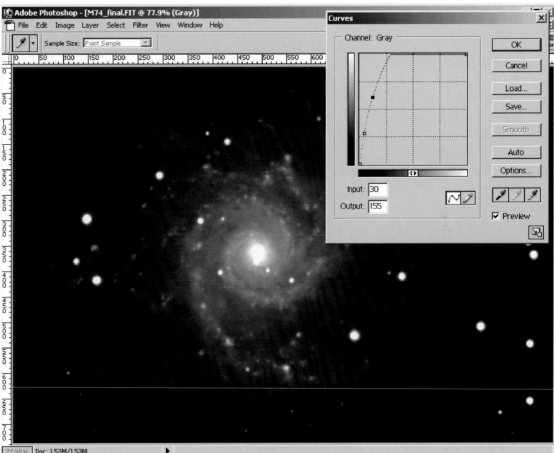

We also still have a large amount of clipping. You might have already guessed at the solution: add another point.

❧ TIP: At this stage of processing the image, it's not critical that you get the location of the Dim and Middle Zone points exactly right. An approximate Standard Curve will work just fine in the early stage of processing.

A Third Point

Adding a third point as shown eliminates clipping and brings the image under control. The Curve shown at right is a Standard Curve. This is a moderately aggressive Standard Curve. The steeper the slope at the Dim Zone point, and the higher overall the curve is, the more aggressive it is. When you are first starting out, use less aggressive Standard Curves. As you learn more about Curves, you can increase the aggressiveness of your approach.

The Standard Curve expands the Dim Zone, revealing dim details. It changes the Middle Zone only slightly, and the Bright Zone is actually compressed.

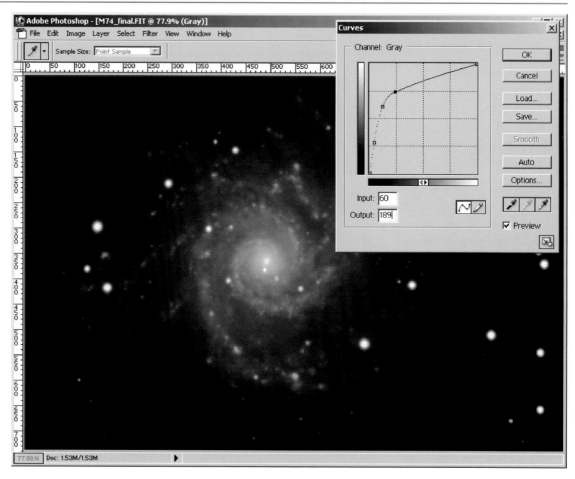

There are 256 brightness levels available for display (because we will eventually output an 8-bit JPG image). At the start, the Dim Zone occupied only a few of these levels—maybe only 1–10%. After Curves, the Dim Zone occupies a larger percentage of the available brightness levels.

Using more brightness levels for dim stuff means we have to take some brightness levels away from the Middle and Bright Zones. You can't gain in one zone without giving something up in another zone. That is why the Bright Zone contracted.

Click OK to save your changes.

The Sweet Spot

The Curve shown on the previous page sits at a particular place on the Curves graph. The question immediately comes up: what if the Curve were lower or higher?

A lower Curve results in a dimmer image, as shown at right. There isn't one perfect curve for any given image. Experiment with each image to find the right vertical position overall for the curve. The best position is based on a combination of your experience and the data in the image.

In most cases, the Dim Zone is such a small percentage of the data that you cannot make a curve aggressive enough to brighten the image in a single pass. Your

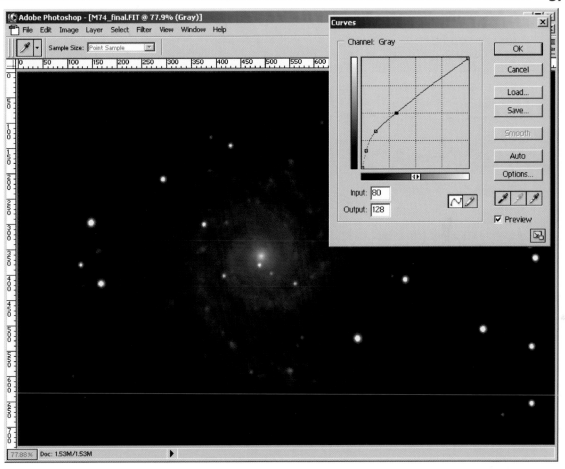

image data is most likely stored with 16 bits of resolution (giving it 65,536 brightness levels). Since Photoshop works at a resolution of only 256 brightness levels (in both Levels and Curves), it's normal to do several iterations of Curves on any given image.

NOTE: You might have noticed that in this and the preceding example the Curve finishes with a straight segment at top right. This "flat-to-the-finish" is a requirement of the Zone System. It controls the Bright Zone, compressing bright portions to allow appropriate expansion of the Dim Zone. A steep slope expands; a flat slope compresses.

A Curve too Far

A Curve that is too aggressive can lead to an image that has a Dim Zone that is *too* bright. However, the more experience you get with the Zone System, the more you will be able to control and work with aggressive curves.

The image at right has a very aggressive curve applied to it. The core of the galaxy is not washed out (thanks to that flat-to-the-finish in the Bright Zone), but it is so bright that it will be challenging to emphasize details in the core. In technical terms, the contrast is compressed in the Bright Zone, leaving little room for emphasizing details. In simplest terms, there are too few brightness levels dedicated to the Bright Zone.

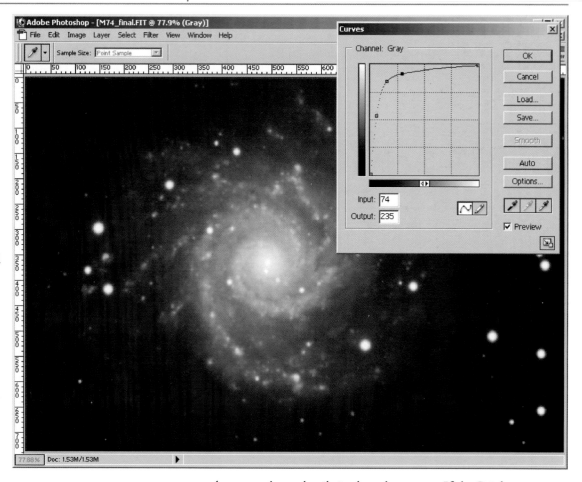

All of the zones need to be balanced with each other so they each have enough brightness levels available. If you over-expand the Dim Zone, the other zones will be compressed and you won't see details in the other zones. If the Bright Zone isn't compressed sufficiently, you won't be able to reveal enough detail in the Dim Zone. This is not so much about technique as it is about a new way of thinking about the image and its processing. That is why we take time to balance between zones when using the Zone System.

Background Control: Levels

Each time you make a change with Curves, you are brightening the dim areas of the image. Even if you imaged under very dark skies, this is also going to brighten the image background. To avoid wasting your histogram changes on the image background, check the black point in Levels after each application of Curves. Raise the black point as needed (see figure at right for an example).

Note that the black point is always raised to a position just to the left of the steep rise in the histogram plot. There is a small tail visible in this example. Such tails can be minor, as here, or quite large. They usually indicate a gradient in the image, but nebulosity or extended areas of nebulosity of dim areas of galaxies can also cause such tails. If raising the black point above the tail removes data from the image, then you should leave the black point below the tail. If raising the black point beyond the tail only removes background, then you are dealing with a gradient. You might be able to clean up the gradient just by putting the black point above the tail, but if not, consider Russell Croman's Gradient XTerminator software:

http://www.rc-astro.com

As you work on the image with multiple iterations of Curves, the histogram changes. The left side of the histogram expands, and the right side of the histogram shrinks (compresses). This reflects what is happening in the image. The dim areas occupy more and more of the available brightness levels (expansion), and the bright areas occupy fewer and fewer (compression).

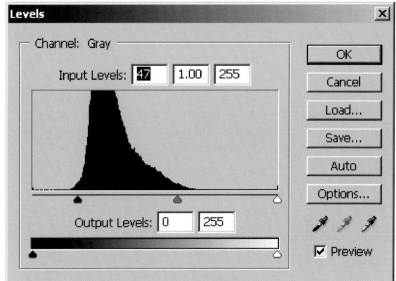

Photoshop CS includes a Histogram palette. This is a small version of the histogram (see below). You can't make changes with the histogram palette; use the Levels tool. The palette is a handy way to watch the histogram as you work with tools. The Histogram palette uses a fast calculation, so it might differ somewhat from the "official" histogram in Levels.

NOTE: Even extremely dark skies have background brightness at some level. The atoms in the air glow in red, for example, and the dust in the solar system also contributes some brightness. Every image will have some need of background control.

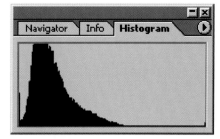

Multiple Passes

For most images, a single Standard Curve will not be sufficient. As described earlier, a single pass offers only a crude level of accuracy in making changes. Multiple passes through Curves allow you to refine the histogram changes and keep them under close control. Multiple passes also allow you to use Levels to converge on the ideal black point for the image.

For the M74 image, I used two passes through Curves. Both passes are shown here for reference. Typically, the first pass (lower left) was aggressive and the second pass (above right)

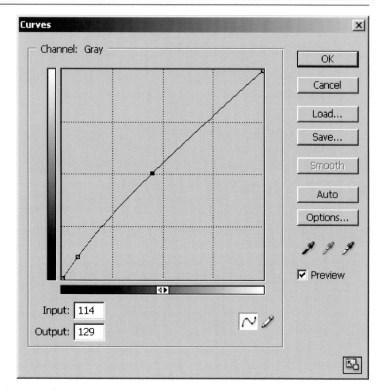

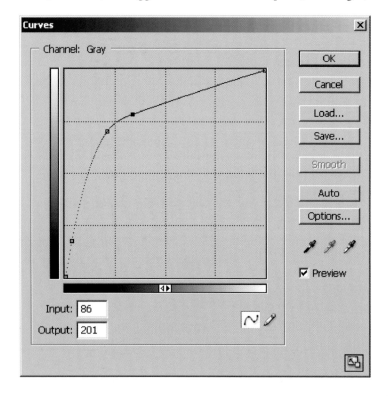

less so. The exact numeric values of each point are not important; the overall shape of the curves is what is important. The "perfect" set of points really depends on what you want to show in the image. Sometimes you will want to emphasize bright details; sometimes you will want to emphasize dim details. Perhaps there is a shock front in a nebula that you want to emphasize, or perhaps you want to reveal details in the bright HII regions of a galaxy as opposed to the dust lanes. No one approach is right or wrong; it depends on what you want to show in the image. As we work through the Zone System, you'll learn exactly how to work with Curves.

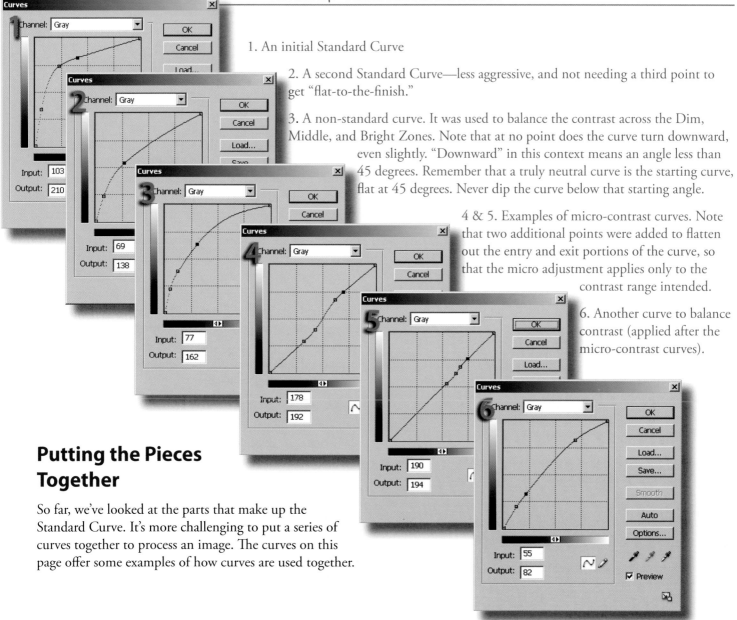

1. An initial Standard Curve

2. A second Standard Curve—less aggressive, and not needing a third point to get "flat-to-the-finish."

3. A non-standard curve. It was used to balance the contrast across the Dim, Middle, and Bright Zones. Note that at no point does the curve turn downward, even slightly. "Downward" in this context means an angle less than 45 degrees. Remember that a truly neutral curve is the starting curve, flat at 45 degrees. Never dip the curve below that starting angle.

4 & 5. Examples of micro-contrast curves. Note that two additional points were added to flatten out the entry and exit portions of the curve, so that the micro adjustment applies only to the contrast range intended.

6. Another curve to balance contrast (applied after the micro-contrast curves).

Putting the Pieces Together

So far, we've looked at the parts that make up the Standard Curve. It's more challenging to put a series of curves together to process an image. The curves on this page offer some examples of how curves are used together.

Review

Basic processing in Photoshop seems simple: just add three points. The key is to add the right three points to create some version of the Standard Curve. You should expect to do multiple iterations of Curves to get the image to look its best.

The first few iterations are not critical. The goal in the early stages is simply to expand the Dim Zone and to compress the Bright Zone. How you get that done is not highly specific. You can use aggressive or non-aggressive Curves. Non-aggressive curves will simply require more iterations.

This is not to say that any old curve will do the trick. Stick with the Standard Curve, which has these characteristics:

- There are three points overall, though the last iteration might only require two points (if there is no clipping and the curve is very non-aggressive).

- The first point roughly represents the Dim Zone. This is true only if you use Levels every time to trim the Dark Zone (by sliding the Black Point to the left of the histogram peak in Levels). Never make this part of the curve so steep that excessive noise is revealed.

- The second point roughly represents the Middle Zone. The job of the second point is to provide a clean transition (a bend on the curve).

- The third point prevents clipping, and should typically be flat-to-the-finish. This compresses the Bright Zone.

- Use progressively less aggressive Standard Curves.

Using the Standard Curve may seem awkward at first, but the more you use it the more you will understand how to control it. At first, you will find yourself guessing. Over time, you will gain an understanding of the subtle changes you can create using variations of the Standard Curve. Here are some tips to help you get started.

- Always add the points from Dim to Bright (left to right). The first point is the most important; it sets the tone for the rest of the process. If the first point is too aggressive, or not aggressive enough, the other two points can't make the image work right.

- Don't hesitate to start over. Try a different location for the initial point, making it higher or lower, further left or further right. Moving a point up and down, or left and right, affects the brightness and contrast of that portion of the image. Such changes are especially critical with the second point because it acts as a pivot point between the Dim and Bright Zones. For more information about vertical and horizontal changes, see chapter 4.

- It takes time to get good at making image adjustments with Curves. The more images you process with Curves, the better your skills will be. Be patient with yourself. It often happens with my students that they work and work and work with Curves, and then suddenly things start to fall into place. Don't give up!

- Work with Curves and Levels in tandem. Attempting to use Curves without setting an appropriate black point results in little or no useful change because you wind up adjusting the Dark Zone instead of the Dim Zone.

Photoshop®
Processing Tips

Photoshop® Processing Tips

Objective

To demonstrate all of the core steps in Photoshop® luminance processing using the Zone System.

Techniques
- Set white point
- Set black point
- Linear and non-linear histogram stretching using the Standard Curve
- Identify dimmest salvageable details
- Set Dim Zone brightness and contrast
- Balance brightness and contrast between zones
- Make micro-contrast adjustments within zones
- Set black point
- Smoothing the Dim Zone
- Sharpening the Bright Zone

Tools
- Photoshop® Levels
- Photoshop® Curves
- Gaussian Blur
- Unsharp Masking
- Color Range...

Description

This chapter demonstrates how to process a luminance image step-by-step in Photoshop®. In addition to working through the tutorial in this chapter, you can solidify your knowledge of the Zone System using the information and tutorials in chapter 2, *Photoshop® Basics: The Standard Curve,* and chapter 4, *Image Processing Workflow.*

Definitions

Black point: A Levels slider for setting the darkest value in the image—all darker values will be rendered black. Used to remove the Dark Zone data from the image.

Clipping: Said of a Curve when it reaches the top line of the graph before reaching the right-hand side of the graph. Effectively lowers the white point, which is often undesirable. Clipping is usually avoided by adding additional points to the right of the existing point(s), and reshaping the Curve so it no longer clips.

Curves: A Photoshop® tool for making non-linear adjustments to the image's histogram. You add points to the curve to control which portions of the data are expanded or contracted. Expansion means that more of the available brightness levels are used for the data; contraction means that fewer brightness levels are used. When more brightness levels are allocated to a region, contrast is said to be stretched in that region. Stretching allows more details to be seen in that region. Since there are a fixed number of brightness levels, if you expand in one region, then you must contract in another. Typically, you expand in the dim areas, and contract in the brighter areas.

Gamma: A slider in the Levels tool that adjusts brightness and contrast simultaneously using a midpoint adjustment. Moving the slider to the left moves the midpoint to a dimmer portion of the image, allocating more brightness levels for the dim portions of the image, which brightens the image overall. See Curves—in a sense, Gamma is a simplified Curve tool.

Grayscale: A palette consisting only of gray values (no color). When you load a FITS image into Photoshop®, it is automatically assigned a Mode of Grayscale.

Histogram: A graph that shows the relative number of pixels at each brightness value. The greater the number of pixels at a given brightness level, the higher the peak. Linear and non-linear changes affect the histogram. You can use the histogram to evaluate how effectively Levels and Curves are modifying the data.

Levels: A Photoshop® tool for making linear adjustments to the image's histogram. See Curves for comparison. Levels is used to adjust the White Point and Black Point (and occasionally the Midpoint for Gamma adjustments).

Linear: Brightness and Contrast adjustments that preserve the internal brightness relationships of the image. Nothing is expanded or contracted. Linear changes are typically limited to changing the White Point and Black Point.

Midpoint: Used to adjust image Gamma. See Gamma.

Non-linear: Brightness and Contrast adjustments that do not preserve internal brightness relationships. One part of the image may get a large boost, while another part may get only a small boost, or even a cut, in brightness and/or contrast.

Points: Added to the Curves dialog to control how much boost or cut each brightness range in the image receives.

White point: A Levels slider for setting the brightest value in the image—all brighter values will be rendered white. Lower the white point when there is no data in the brightest values.

Open a File

The image at right shows what you will see when you open the image for this tutorial (see box at bottom right). This is an extraordinary image of the Cocoon Nebula—7.5 hours of data, in the form of 13 30-minute images. The images were taken with a 20" Ritchie-Chrétien telescope and STL-11000 camera at my observatory in New Mexico.

Because of the long exposures, quite a few stars show up clearly even before you do any histogram processing on the image.

Due to the extremely long total exposure time, and the long individual exposures, there are some things we can say about this image:

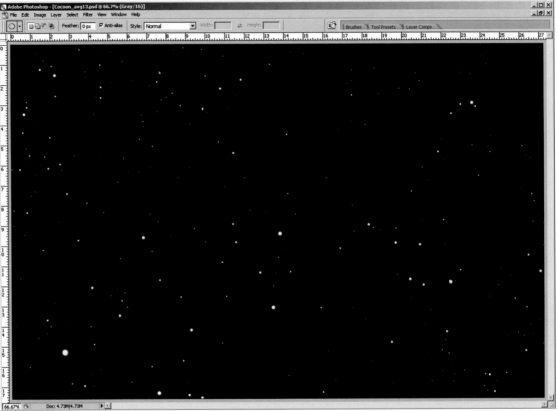

- Read noise will be a small portion of the total noise
- A large portion of the image will be in the Bright Zone

In fact, portions of the image that aren't very bright will still technically be in the Bright Zone because it is S/N (signal-to-noise ratio) that determines zones, not absolute brightness.

The terms Dim, Middle, and Bright are helpful for average images. But you'll need to keep S/N in mind when working with very short or very long exposure times.

If you would like to follow along with this exercise, open the following file from the DVD in Photoshop® CS (or later):

\C3\Cocoon_avg13.fit

Set White/Black Points

When you open a raw image in Photoshop®, you need to set the data range you want to work with. Use the *Image » Adjustments » Levels* menu item.

If necessary, lower the white point to the top of the histogram. In this case, the histogram plot goes all the way to the right. It's a thin line, but it is there! No white point adjustment is needed.

If there is a gap to the left of the main peak (as above left), move the Black Point slider to the right, to a point that is a little bit to the left of the peak (as shown). Leave a little room for error; you will refine the black point as you progress. Click OK to save your changes in Levels.

Next, open the *Image » Adjustments » Curves* menu item. Click on the curve (it's just a diagonal line to start) near bottom left and drag this point upward. Because (and only because) you adjusted the black and white points correctly, this point corresponds to the Dim Zone. This is the first point on the Standard Curve. Calculate the slope as Output divided by Input. In this case, the slope is 88/15, or about 6:1. That's slightly aggressive. Slopes from 4:1 to 6:1 are typically used.

The Standard Curve typically has three points on it: one at the bottom left that corresponds to the Dim Zone; one at the middle left for the Middle Zone; and one at the top right to create flat-to-the-finish for the Bright Zone. See chapter 2, *Photoshop® Basics: The Standard Curve*, for more details.

❧ Tıp: Whatever aggressiveness you choose for the Standard Curve, base it on your comfort level. As you gain experience using the Standard Curve, you will be able to use more aggressive curves.

If you are just starting out, follow some simple rules for the Standard Curve:

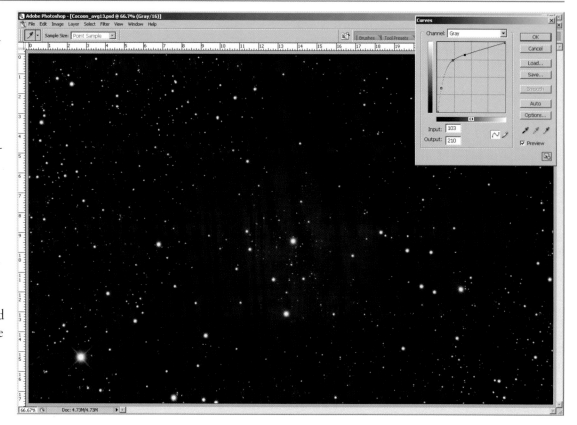

- Place the point for the Dim Zone at the one-third position within the left horizontal quadrant of the graph. (You raise it vertically to get expansion in the Dim Zone.)
- Place the point for the Middle Zone in the first quadrant, between the 75% and 100% position horizontally. In the figure above, the Middle Zone point is close to the 100% position within the first quadrant.
- The job of the Middle Zone point is to create a transition.

The steep slope to the left of this point is expanding the number of brightness slots available to the Dim Zone. The flat-to-the-finish slope to the right compresses the number of slots used by the Bright Zone. Start with a reasonably gentle curve between these two slopes. As your skills advance, you can use a tighter curve for this transition.

- Be careful not to create a reverse curve with the Bright Zone point. Aim for flat-to-the-finish. You can use a different Bright Zone curve later, during final tweaking.

Refine the Black Point

It is typical (and common) to use the Standard Curve more than once. Even for this very deep exposure of the Cocoon, the initial histogram peak is still fairly narrow. It will take several applications of the Standard Curve to expand the Dim Zone far enough to please the eye.

❧ Tɪᴘ: The main benefit to more aggressive Standard Curves is that you can cut down on the number of times you use Curves. However, less aggressive curves give you more control, and are less challenging to construct.

❧ Tɪᴘ: I am being relentless about reminding you to use Levels to adjust the black point after every application of a Standard Curve. But you really *do* need to check the black point every time you use Curves. This includes tweaking and micro-contrast adjustments.

The figure at right shows the appropriate adjustment to the black point following the first application of the Standard Curve.

The rule remains the same: move the black point slider in Levels rightward, until it is just before the main peak. If you are just starting out, leave enough room to make absolutely certain you aren't removing real data from the image.

If you move the slider past the correct point, and it winds up inside the peak, then you are likely to be throwing away some of the Dim Zone. Be careful to leave yourself a safety margin, and stay to the left of the main peak.

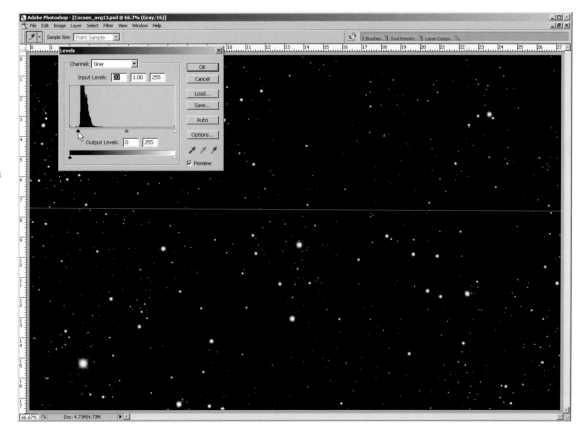

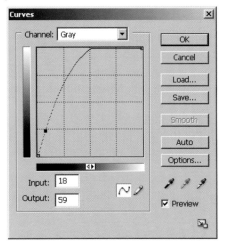 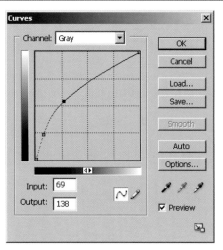

If you are looking around for the figure that shows the third point on the curve, you can stop looking. This curve only has two points, but it's still a perfectly valid Standard Curve.

Because the first point is not aggressive, the second point is capable of doing two jobs:

- Creating the transition curve normally accomplished with the Middle Zone point.
- Establishing the flat-to-the-finish portion of the curve normally associated with the Bright Zone point.

Iterate Standard Curve/Black Point

❧ Tip: The first Standard Curve is always the most aggressive. Even if you use a non-aggressive initial curve, subsequent curves are typically less aggressive.

For the second curve, I used an especially non-aggressive curve (see the two figures above). I want to reinforce the idea that the exact aggressiveness of the curve isn't the important thing. The overall construction of the curve simply has to meet the requirements described on the previous pages.

The above figures illustrate this. The left image above shows the location of the Dim Zone point. This is always the first point you place. It is located where it belongs—in the left half of the left quadrant. The slope in this case is 59/18, or 3:1.

❧ Tip: While slopes of 4:1 to 6:1 are typical for the initial Standard Curve, lower (and sometimes much lower) slopes often occur on subsequent applications of Curves.

The right-hand point accomplishes this magic by being in exactly the right place. Note that although this point is doing the Middle Zone point's job, it's a little further right than one would usually expect. This is a compromise horizontal position, and is typical when you are creating a two-point Standard Curve.

It is important to note that a two-point Standard Curve isn't the only option at this point in processing. You could still use three points even with the non-aggressive Dim Zone point. You could use a completely different, and more aggressive, curve with two or three points.

As long as the curve meets the fundamental requirements of the Standard Curve, it will get the job done. The only difference will be the number of times you go through the Curves dialog as you process the image.

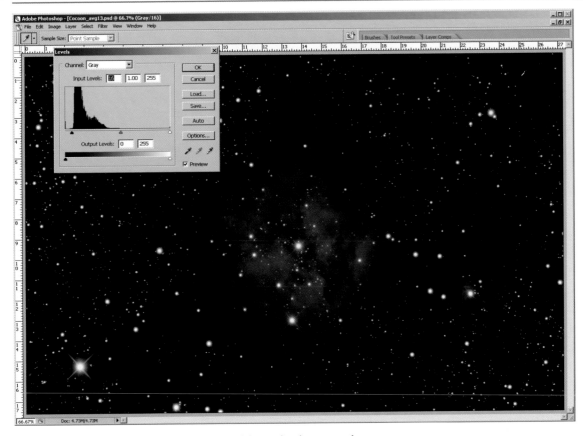

the Bright Zone (at right) is being compressed. The Dim Zone now occupies nearly half of the available brightness slots. The dim details of the Cocoon are now clearly visible, as are many of the dimmer stars.

The Dark Zone gets expanded along with the Dim Zone. That is why the gap at the left side of the histogram reappears after every use of Curves. This is why you go back into Levels after every application of Curves. You are using Levels to refine the position of the black point.

The purpose of the black point adjustment is to remove the Dark Zone. The more you expand the dark/dim portions of the image, the more accurately you can set the black point. You should always leave the black point a little left of the main peak so that the background stays slightly gray; this allows the eye to see dim details better.

Any use of Curves is always followed by a check-up on the black point using Levels, as shown above.

Note that after two applications of the Standard Curve, the shape of the histogram is changing dramatically. The once narrow peak has broadened considerably. This reflects what is being accomplished by the repeated applications of the Standard Curve: the Dim Zone (at left) is being expanded, and

After two or three Standard Curves, you are usually ready to identify the brightness level of the dimmest details.

The steep slope of the temporary curve is useful for identifying the dimmest details in the Dim Zone. These are the dimmest details you can show in the image after processing.

The question immediately arises: "OK, but how do I tell which details are the dimmest in the Dim Zone?" You don't want to include the Dark Zone, after all!

The trick, of course, lies as always with the signal-to-noise ratio (S/N). Somewhere in the image, the noise level is (usually) high enough to create so much uncertainty that you can't tell if the details are real. When you see so much grain or read noise residue that you are unsure whether the details you are looking at are real or noise, the answer is: they are noise, and are part of the Dark Zone. You want to settle on dim details that are clearly real, clearly something you can show in the image after some smoothing. Heavy grain or banding rules out inclusion in the image.

Set Brightness of Dimmest Details

Open Curves and create a very aggressive Dim Zone point as above. This is a temporary curve that you can use to see where the Dim Zone details are.

❧ TIP: If you create a steep curve, and you still can't see the dimmest Dim Zone details, then you need at least one more application of the Standard Curve before you try this stuff.

Once you can *see* these dimmest details, you can use a nifty feature of the Curves dialog to determine the exact brightness level of the details. The red arrow on the facing page shows the Curves cursor. It is located on some of the dimmest details in the image. Clicking on this area causes an open circle to appear momentarily on the curve (see Curves dialog at upper right, facing page). It also causes the brightness value of these details to show up as Input.

The Input value is 12. Your value will likely be different. The value depends on the Curves and Levels processing choices you make. As long as you set the correct black point, however, this will work OK.

Once you have this brightness value, you can close the Curves dialog. Or you can click and drag the existing point outside the graph to remove it.

Re-open Curves (if necessary), and click to add a point near the lower left. It doesn't matter if it is exactly at the Input level you identified earlier. Edit the Input value: click in the Input box, and enter the brightness level you found earlier (see figure at lower left). Try various brightness values in the Output box until the Dim Zone details are visible. Generally, unless there is something really special about the details, you simply want to make them bright enough to be visible.

The two images above show the wrong and the right way to handle the next step: balancing contrast between zones.

The Curve in the image at top left looks like a Standard Curve. This yields a flat image with poor contrast.

In the upper right image, each point corresponds to a zone. Move points up or down to balance the contrast between zones. The differences in the Middle and Bright Zone points make a major difference in the appearance of the images.

- Middle Zone point is much lower. This is the key difference; now the Middle Zone is a little darker and can be visually separated from the Bright Zone.
- The Bright Zone point is lower and left, which allows the curve to really *curve* in the Bright Zone. This creates a range of brightness levels throughout the Bright Zone.

As always, set the black point to the left of the main peak in Levels, as shown in the figure at lower right.

Micro-Contrast

The sequence of images on the facing page shows how to set, and adjust, points for a micro-contrast adjustment (intra-zone contrast).

Micro-contrast alters the contrast relationships of similarly bright areas in all parts of the image, so I recommend evaluating the result carefully.

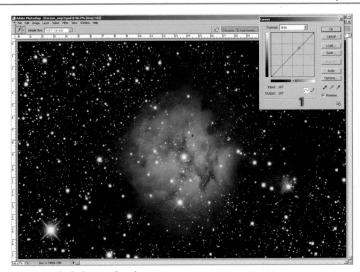

1. Control-click on a brighter area

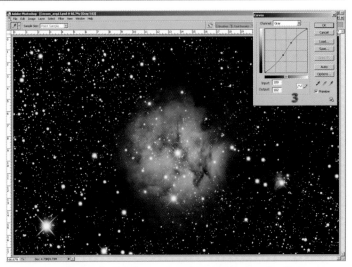

3. Increase Output for brighter point; decrease Output for dimmer point.

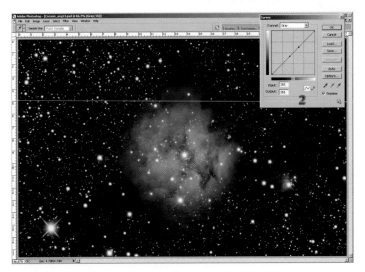

2. Control-click on a dimmer adjoining area

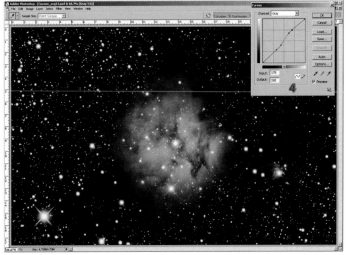

4. Add control points to flatten all other portions of the curve (above and below the micro-contrast points).

at least slightly brighter than the other). The brighter point has been moved up, and the dimmer point has been moved downward. Control points have been added to the curve to straighten out the balance of the curve above and below the micro-contrast adjustment.

The flat portions confine the changes to only the region you are interested in changing with the micro-contrast adjustment.

The image above shows a more extreme example of a micro-contrast adjustment. The region where the contrast adjustment occurs is shown at lower right (the brighter region is being selected).

Note: Even though the points on the curve are very close together, the overall arrangement of points is just like the earlier example. There are two points that were created by control-clicking on adjoining brightness values (one must be

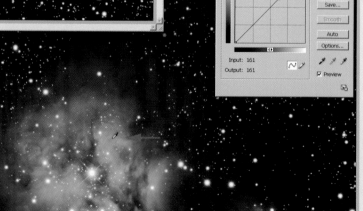

Final Tweaking with Curves

There is usually some data somewhere that we haven't yet managed to include in the visible portion of the image, or that is out of balance with respect to the rest of the image. In this example, we have an image with an exceptionally low level of noise (and thus very high S/N) in the Dim Zone. A final tweak with Curves will bring out the dimmest details, while avoiding over-brightening or other problems as a result of this adjustment.

The curve in the image at right has three points, but these do not correspond exactly to the Zones. This late in the process, you are more likely to identify a specific brightness level that needs adjustment than to want to change an entire zone. But both are possible.

As always, add the points from left to right. The left point does correspond to a zone—the Dim Zone. Look again at the image on the facing page. The entire Dim Zone is underrepresented. It's barely visible. The point has been moved up, so the Dim Zone is brighter.

The second point is at the lowest end of the Bright Zone. There is a subtle shift in slope which causes this brightness level to get less boost than the Dim Zone. This point also functions to provide a transition—lots of boost to the Dim Zone; moderate boost to the low end of the Middle Zone. The third point is fairly far up in the Bright Zone, and is solving a completely different problem: the Bright Zone needs a little boost to bring out the rich contrast possibilities.

Selecting Dim Zone for Smoothing

The Dim Zone in this image is pretty smooth, but I can still use it as an example for how to do smoothing with the Color Range tool. Use the *Select» Color Range...* menu item to open this dialog. Make sure that Fuzziness is around 40, and that Quick Mask is the Selection Preview setting.

As shown at top left, click in the darkest part of the image to start the selection. Next, click on the middle eyedropper icon. This changes to a plus cursor; when you click, it adds to the selection. Continue clicking on progressively brighter areas until the edge of the unselected portion (red) loses its grainy appearance. You don't need to get rid of all signs of graininess, just go to the point where it is cut down significantly.

Click OK to actually create the selection (facing page).

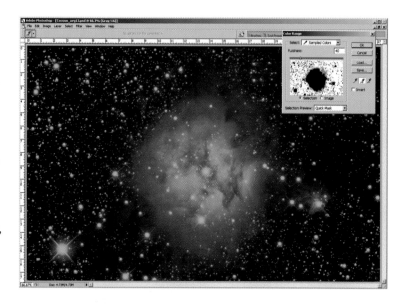

The selection that results from use of the Color Range tool can be very complex, especially if there are lots of stars in the field as in this example (see figure below). This isn't a problem in any way, however. A zone is a zone is a zone.

But zones don't have hard edges, and coming out of the Color Range tool the selection has semi-hard boundaries. The fuzziness factor will result in a soft (feathered) edge in areas of nebulosity, but around stars the boundary is very firm.

menu item to back off the selection. The amount depends on the star size in pixels, but values of 3–7 are typical. For this example, contract by 4 pixels.

A bit of feathering to soften the edge between the stars and the selection area is necessary. A feather of 50–75% of the contraction value is about right. In this example, I am applying a feather of 3 pixels. The feather extends both inside and outside of the selection boundary.

This presents some problems for both smoothing and sharpening. You don't want a hard, noticeable edge between zones.

There is a second problem: the Gaussian Blur (the only smoothing tool in Photoshop® that is useful for astro images) will include a star in the blur *even if the star is outside the boundary of the selection*—but only if the star is close enough to that boundary. The solution: use the *Select»Modify»Contract*

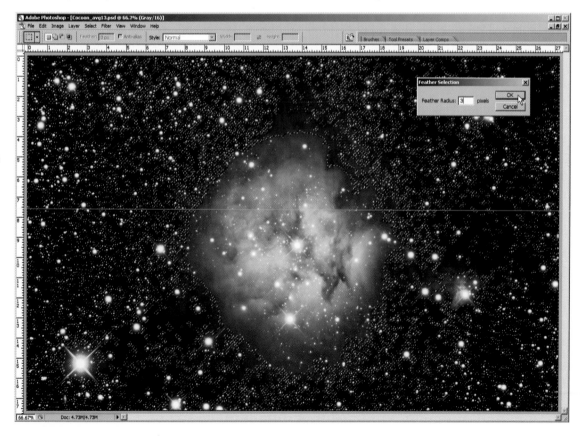

Smoothing the Dim Zone

Smoothing is done with the *Filter » Blur » Gaussian Blur...* menu item. The dialog, shown below at left, has a single adjustment: radius of the blur in pixels. Useful blur values are from 0.3 (extremely light blur) to 1.2 (a heavy but manageable blur). Smaller blur values have no effect. Larger blur values fail for two reasons: they look artificial, and no value is large enough to cover up severe noise. Severe noise defines the Dark Zone, and should be removed using Levels and the black point adjustment.

☙ Tip: If you have CS2 or later, you can use the *Filter » Noise » Reduce Noise* menu item. See chapter 4 for details on using this tool for smoothing.

Sharpening the Bright Zone

Before you can sharpen the bright zone, you need to select it. There are many selection tools in Photoshop®, but for this example, I demonstrate a combination approach: an initial selection to define which portion of the Bright Zone we want to work on, and then the Color Range tool to select just the useful portions of the Bright Zone within the initial selection.

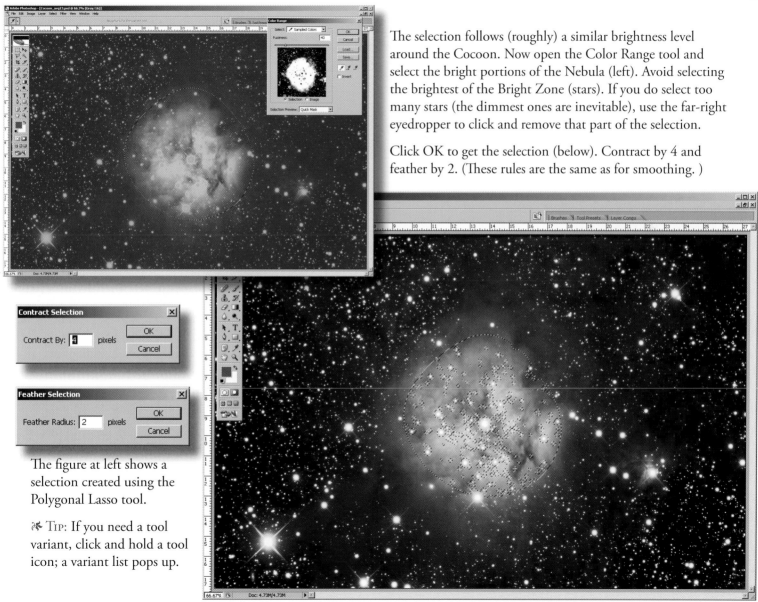

The selection follows (roughly) a similar brightness level around the Cocoon. Now open the Color Range tool and select the bright portions of the Nebula (left). Avoid selecting the brightest of the Bright Zone (stars). If you do select too many stars (the dimmest ones are inevitable), use the far-right eyedropper to click and remove that part of the selection.

Click OK to get the selection (below). Contract by 4 and feather by 2. (These rules are the same as for smoothing.)

The figure at left shows a selection created using the Polygonal Lasso tool.

Tip: If you need a tool variant, click and hold a tool icon; a variant list pops up.

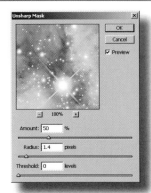

The image at left shows how to set up large-feature sharpening. A Threshold value of 2–4 is typical; try 4 and work down if that value is excessive. A starting amount of 80% and a radius of 4 are also good starting points. Adjust radius first, lowering Threshold if you think the sharpening isn't aggressive enough. Worst case, reduce the amount by 10–20%.

You have now selected the portion of the Bright Zone we want to sharpen. You could have included the stars, but then the stars over the nebula would be sharper than the stars in the background.

Use the *Filter»Sharpen»Unsharp Mask...* menu item. I recommend two types of sharpening: large-feature sharpening, which uses a non-zero Threshold setting, and fine-feature sharpening, which uses a zero Threshold setting.

The figure at top right shows good starting settings for fine-feature sharpening. I rarely touch the Amount and Threshold values. I adjust the radius to sharpen however much the noise level in the region being sharpened allows. When following large-feature sharpening, a setting below 2 pixels for the radius is usually necessary. In this example, I sharpened using a radius of 1.4 pixels.

See chapter 4 for details of the techniques used here.

Image Processing Workflow

Image Processing Workflow

Overview

There are many steps involved in processing an image. Some things you do all the time; other things you do when they are needed. This chapter provides a comprehensive list of the steps involved in image processing, from data reduction to final tweaking. This chapter is a reference that goes deeper, and offers more insights, than the tutorials found elsewhere in the book.

Details

There are five phases in processing an image. Things like setup, preparation, configuration, and most issues related to acquisition are covered in Imaging Workflow 1. There is a sixth phase as well: Imaging decisions. In addition to the five phases, the decisions you make before and during imaging affect what you can do when you are processing your images. For information about workflow during imaging, as opposed to image *processing,* please see this bonus chapter on the DVD:

> \bonus\workflow1.pdf

The five phases involved in image processing are:

Data Reduction   (Also called calibration) Removing instrument (system) artifacts from the data. Some would expand this step to include hot/cold pixel removal (and rejection of outliers such as cosmic ray hits).

Color Balancing   The process of balancing the contribution of the red, green, and blue channels to each other. Includes color bias removal (aka background normalization), color balancing, noise-related issues, and saturation.

Histogram   Includes both linear and non-linear histogram changes. Linear changes (Levels) set the background. Non-linear changes (Curves) expand the Dim Zone and compress the Bright Zone.

Zonal Processing   Applying specific types of processing to the different zones, such as smoothing the Dim Zone and sharpening the Bright Zone.

Cleanup   Some types of cleanup can be done at any time during image processing, but some types of cleanup are easier to do after you are nearly done with the image. Cleanup includes removing hot and cold pixels, tweaking contrast to enhance details, removing gradients, removing halos around stars, etc.

Imaging Decisions

Imaging is a data collection process. You can make better decisions about your imaging by learning some of the foundation concepts involved in statistics and data collection.

What I'm trying to say here is that imaging is really a form of sampling. Collecting a single sample isn't very informative. If you were measuring chimpanzee behavior, watching one chimp might be interesting but not necessarily representative. For example, if that one chimp is in the habit of scratching his nose before eating, it would not be safe to assume that all chimps scratch their nose before they eat.

Likewise, if you take a single image, you might wind up with a cosmic ray striking the CCD chip and creating a streak or, worse, a false star. By taking more than one image of a subject, you can get closer to the truth of what you are imaging. This is true of all data collection, not just imaging.

Individual Exposure Times

With few exceptions, longer exposure times are better than shorter for deep-sky objects. This is based on the nature of noise. Noise is not an intuitive subject, and it's easy to get to the wrong answer if you aren't careful with your assumptions. I've provided links below to detailed mathematical treatments of the noise question for those who want to pursue them.

The rest of us need a convenient way to visualize the problems that noise causes. The simplest approach is to acknowledge that more noise is bad, and less noise is good. The goal is to keep the noise level down.

To get a better grasp on what noise does to your images, I suggest some linguistic trickery. Replace the word *noise* with the word **uncertainty.** Because that's what noise really is: uncertainty in the data. (And this won't be the last time you'll see that word "data," either.)

For example, if the readout noise level is 10 electrons (abbreviated 10^{e-}), then we know that the number of electrons is uncertain by that amount. Suppose the camera counts 100^{e-} for a certain pixel. Due to the uncertainty, the actual count could be anywhere from 95^{e-} to 105^{e-}.

For bright pixels, this level of uncertainty isn't a big deal. But it is usually the dim portions of the image that are the most interesting. An uncertainty of 10^{e-} means a lot more when the electron count is 20 than it does when the electron count is 20,000. The electron count is the signal in the data.

So it makes sense to expand the definition of the goal: Keep the noise level down, and the signal level high. Things like higher quantum efficiency, longer individual exposures, and more total exposure time all contribute to success.

How Much Blooming Can You Live with?

If your camera blooms, this will set an upper limit on your exposure time. There are convenient deblooming software tools available, but they work best when blooms are not excessive. A bloom represents missing data, and if blooms are too large, the missing data is too much for the software tools to deal with. (It's worth noting that deblooming software only makes the image look better by removing the bloom; the software can't replace the data that was blocked by the bloom!)

Whether you debloom manually or with software (or not at all), you'll need to be aware of the maximum blooming level you can tolerate. For a given camera/telescope combination, the amount of blooming depends on the brightness of the stars involved and the length of the exposure.

If you have a camera that does not bloom, you can (almost) take images as long as you care to. Some non-blooming cameras create larger and larger bright stars as the exposure continues, and for such cameras the size of the stars might limit your exposure times as much as blooming would. For more recent anti-blooming cameras, long exposures under dark skies can work wonders (try 30 minutes or more).

Background Level

The brightness of your sky will determine the background level for a given exposure time with your equipment. However, once your background level hits a certain point, there is little or no advantage to taking a longer single exposure.

Reducing Contribution of Read Noise

The reason for taking long exposures is simple. Long exposures limit the contribution of readout noise. Readout noise (often called simply read noise) is constant. You get the same amount of read noise for any single exposure. So a long exposure has the same amount of read noise as a short exposure.

In simplest terms, the shot noise from a long exposure swamps the contribution from read noise. For information on what shot noise is, how it is measured, and why this is important, please see chapter 1, *The Zone System.*

Avoiding Overly Bright Background

An overly bright background limits the dynamic range of your images. If your camera saturates at a brightness level of 50,000, and your background level is 25,000, then you are only using 25,000 brightness levels.

Since background levels of 1,000 to 3,000 are enough to swamp the read noise, an exposure that gives you that background level is long enough. This is called a sky-limited exposure (the noise from sky brightness dominates the read noise).

Each type of CCD chip has a background level where read noise will be swamped. CCDWare has a web page where you can learn how long of an exposure will swamp read noise for your camera and sky brightness level:

http://www.ccdware.com/resources/subexposure.cfm

If you would like to get the in-depth info on read noise, exposure times, shot noise, and other topics, try these links:

http://home.earthlink.net/~stanleymm/eXtreme.htm

http://www.hiddenloft.darkhorizons.org/notes/acq.htm

NOTE: If you are imaging from a very dark location, you might not be able to take long enough images to swamp the read noise. At my location in New Mexico, under very dark skies, it would take me more than 90 minutes to get a single sky-limited exposure with my STL-11000. This almost makes dark skies sound like a bad thing! But it simply means that the sky noise is so low that, for any reasonable exposure time, read noise will be more of a factor than light pollution will.

Exposure Times for ABG Cameras

Anti-blooming cameras follow the preceding exposure recommendations, but are otherwise a different ball game. Since there is no blooming, the upper limit on exposure time is based on background saturation. The issue of read noise versus background level still applies. Because of the lower quantum efficiency of ABG cameras, you might need to expose about twice as long to get the desired background level.

As noted earlier, some older ABG cameras tend to create larger stars with longer exposures. This can also influence your choice of exposure time.

The bottom line for individual exposure time is to try to expose at least long enough to swamp the read noise, limited by blooming and/or sky brightness. This is the optimal single exposure time for your location.

Total Exposure Time

Simply put, you can't have too much exposure time. A long total exposure time reduces noise, so it is always desirable.

The rate at which longer exposure times reduce noise isn't 1:1. That is, if you double your total exposure time, you do not cut the noise in half. This is where the mathematical nature of noise makes itself known. As you increase the number of exposures, noise reduction is equal to the *square root* of the number of exposures. This means that you would need to expose four times as long to cut noise in half. Doubling your exposure time yields 1.42 better noise levels (that's the square root of two).

It's not a big deal to cut your noise in half by going from one two-minute exposure to four two-minute exposures. But if you want those incredibly deep, gorgeous images, you'll be needing four hours instead of one hour to cut your noise in half for long exposures. This is why you see a decreasing return per exposure as you take more exposures.

Cooling

CCD cameras, unlike digital cameras, include powerful cooling capabilities in the form of thermoelectric coolers (TEC). A TEC uses electricity to pump heat away from the CCD. This creates a heat load that has to be carried away or it will heat up the camera. Many cameras have fans to blow the heat away from the camera. Some cameras include liquid cooling options as well. Professionals take cooling to an extreme; they use heavy-duty TEC and/or liquid nitrogen to cool the CCD chip much more than amateur cameras can do.

But dramatic cooling isn't required to get good results. Most of the chips in use in amateur CCD cameras deliver very good results with moderate cooling. Typical amateur cameras will be able to cool to a temperature somewhere in the range of –15°C to –40°C, even in warm weather. (Typical cameras can cool from 25°C to 60°C below ambient temperature.)

The cooling does a very simple thing: it lowers the energy level of the CCD chip. With less energy available, there are fewer wandering electrons around. These wandering electrons are called by various names—thermal electrons, thermal current, dark current, etc. By cooling the CCD chip, the number of thermal electrons is reduced.

Even so, there will still be some of these electrons wandering into pixels. The good news is that most pixels are reasonably consistent about the number of thermal electrons they will absorb in a given amount of time at a given temperature. Dark frames record the thermal current, and for most cameras, you can use dark frames to remove the thermal current.

NOTE: There is a noise penalty when subtracting dark frames to correct the dark current. The source is the same as for images: there is always some readout noise (uncertainty) for any image. In mathematical terms, the total noise is the square root of the sum of the squares of the noise levels (root mean square, RMS) from the various noise sources. The name *RMS* is based on how the result is calculated: it is the square root of the mean of the squares of the noise sources.

The bottom line on cooling is that more is better, but with diminishing returns once you get into the –20 to –25˚C for most cameras.

NOTE: Some cameras are designed with special low-noise chips that do not require cooling. One example is the Starlight XPress SXV-H9. These are surprisingly effective.

For best results, always run the cooler below its maximum capacity. For small- to medium-size CCD chips, stay below about 80%. For very large chips, stay below 60%.

Guiding Advice

There are two fundamentally different ways to guide: using some portion of the imaging telescope's optical path, and using an external guide scope.

Built-in Guider Chip/Off-Axis Guiding

To use the imaging telescope's optical path for guiding, you typically need a pick-off mirror to deflect some portion of the incoming light to a second chip or CCD camera. This is in many ways the easiest way to guide because once you set it up, it just works. The guider and the imager are using the same physical system, so anything that might move (for example, a primary mirror that shifts) affects both the guider and the imager identically. Guider corrections will compensate for any such movement as long as it isn't too large or too fast.

There are some disadvantages to this approach, however. If the guide camera or chip is behind the same filters used for the imaging chip, the guide star will be dimmed. And if the shutter is closed on a camera with a built-in guide chip (e.g., SBIG ST and STL series cameras), guiding has to stop until the shutter re-opens. Finally, a built-in guider or off-axis guider uses the same focal length as the imaging chip (by definition), and this limits the number of guide stars available.

Overall, however, self-guiding cameras are extremely convenient, external guiders are not, and so most imagers graduate to third-party off-axis guiders or external guiders only when it becomes essential to do so.

External Guide Scope

External guide scopes introduce a mix of issues into the guiding process. The longer your focal length, and the smaller the pixels on your imaging CCD chip, the more likely you are to have to engage in some problem solving before you can guide successfully.

Advantages

The primary advantage of an external guide scope is that it frees you from the minor tyrannies of internal guiding. You can continue guiding during downloads, for example, because the external guider has its own shutter. It is not affected by any filters you are using for imaging—all the available light from the guide star reaches the guider.

Another important advantage is that the external guider, by definition, uses its own optical system. This means you can use a widefield telescope as your guide scope. This makes it much easier to locate guide stars.

Disadvantages

The primary disadvantage of an external guide scope is that it is a separate optical system. Even if you attach the guide scope to the telescope (and the camera to the guide scope) very rigidly, you can still wind up with differential flexure between the two optical systems.

Resolving differential flexure problems can be challenging. Sometimes, however, you just get lucky. A good example of this is a C14 that I used for imaging several years ago. I carefully set up a Brandon 90mm achromat as my external guider. I added six set screws to the focuser tube so that I could lock the tube solidly into place, added three more set screws for the camera, and bolted the entire assembly to the side of the C14. From the very first, it guided very well despite the long focal length of the C14. I was able to take 15-minute guided exposures without problems.

Thinking myself wise to upgrade to an apochromat as my guider, I sold the Brandon and bought a 90mm APO (Takahashi Sky90). Despite my best efforts, I was never able to clear up the differential flexure with the new setup, and was never able to guide longer than about 5–7 minutes.

The lesson here is that you cannot predict what you will need to do to achieve quality external guiding. The longer the focal length of your telescope, the harder it is to get good external guiding. In many cases, you'll need to play detective in order to figure out where the differential flexure is coming from.

There is one other potential disadvantage of an external guide scope: cost. You can get very good guiding with an achromatic refractor, and even ED refractors represent a good value. But the temptation will be there to get a fast APO as your guide scope. If you go that route, you can also use it for widefield imaging. Even the better ED achromats can make good widefield imaging telescopes. The ED scopes from Hutech are an especially good value, and are used by many for both guiding and widefield imaging.

Dithering

Dithering is the process of shifting images so that they are slightly misaligned. The purpose of dithering is to make sure that repeating artifacts (such as hot pixels) do not line up in the images. When you combine, and especially if you are using some form of statistical data rejection, the hot pixels will be cleaned up very effectively if the images are dithered. If you dither, plan on at least 8–10 images so you can use the most effective data-rejection tools.

Image Processing: Luminance

There isn't a dramatic difference in the processing of luminance (L) and color (RGB) images. However, most imagers take their color and luminance images separately, so it is worth addressing the requirements separately. This workflow assumes that you have taken a series of luminance images, and a series of red, green, and blue (RGB) images, and wish to combine them into an LRGB image.

Noise Control

Noise control is fundamental to all image processing. The lower the noise, the more accurately you can process the data. (Uncertainty becomes magnified during processing.) The lower the noise, the more you can process without adversely affecting the image quality.

Data Reduction

Also known as image calibration, data reduction is the process of removing artifacts and system noise, and reducing random noise, in the data. I prefer the term "data reduction" simply because it puts the focus on what is really going on. Although the final desired outcome is an image, what you are really doing is processing data to get to that image.

Artifact removal consists of such things as correcting for bad pixels, columns, or rows. System noise is mostly present in the form of dark current, the slow leak of electrons into pixels. Noise reduction involves nothing more than increasing the sample size to get a more accurate result.

One-Shot Color Cameras

Some CCD cameras take color images in one shot, such as the ST-2000XMC and the SXV-H9C. You can enjoy the advantages of separate luminance and RGB processing even if you are using a one-shot color camera.

The advantages of separate processing are similar to the advantages of the Zone System. There are processing steps (e.g., sharpening) that are easiest to control and evaluate when working with purely luminance data. Likewise, some color processing steps (e.g., color noise reduction, color balancing) are easier done with pure color data.

It is very easy to create separate luminance and color layers from the output of a one-shot color camera. You can do the conversion at the very beginning of your processing, or at any time during standard processing.

1. Duplicate the *Background* layer, and name the copy RGB (this will be the color layer).

2. Select the *Background* layer (click on the layer name).

3. Use the *Image»Adjustments»Desaturate* menu item to remove color data from the Background layer. This is now the luminance layer.

4. Select the RGB layer.

5. Set the *blend mode* of the RGB layer to *Color*. This is now the color layer.

You can now process the image conventionally.

Combine Requirements

I have made a strong case for taking a large number of images and for a long total exposure time. Both of these steps will go a long way toward lowering noise (and thus uncertainty) in your data. However, the best method to use for combining those individual images varies.

There are three basic types of combining: average, median, and fancy. Each has its place in the scheme of things.

Average Combine

Mathematically, an average combine is the Gold Standard of combining. It always yields the lowest noise. Even so, an average combine is not always the best choice.

How can this be? How can the very best combination method ever not be, ahem, the best way to go? It comes down to what you mean by "best."

Best, in the mathematical sense, is easy to define. The combine method that provides the highest possible S/N is the best method. Average combine always provides the highest signal to noise ratio. (That is, the uncertainty in the data is always least with an average combine.)

But visually an average combine has some weaknesses. The biggest weakness has to do with *outliers.* These are data points that are far from the average value. They occur most commonly when a cosmic ray strikes the CCD detector, but they can also include such things as satellite trails or even stars in a flat-field image. Outliers typically make up a very small portion of the data, but visually even a single outlier is noticeable.

Averaging doesn't get rid of outliers very effectively. Worse, it shifts the average value in favor of the outlier. Even if you combine ten images, one image with a cosmic ray hit will leave a visible trace of the cosmic ray's trail.

For example, consider the values of a particular pixel location in five different images. Without a cosmic ray hit, you might get a string of values like this in five images:

2341 2344 2338 2340 2345» average = 2341.6

Look what happens if a cosmic ray hit exists in one image:

2341 2344 41234 2340 2345» average = 10120.8

The presence of the outlier has completely thrown things into a tizzy. The value is way out of line with reality, and even with five images the cosmic ray hit will be obvious.

 Tip: If you only have a few outliers in your image, you can use Photoshop®'s Clone Tool or Healing Brush to clean them up manually. This allows you to get the best advantages of average combining and still get rid of the outliers.

Median Combine

A median combine, on the other hand, handles outliers well. A median is simply the middle value in a series. Consider the cosmic ray example from the discussion of average combine. If we arrange the values in order:

2340 2341 2344 2345 41234

The middle value is 2344, which, as luck would have it, is reasonably close to the average value of 2341.6 from the non-cosmic-ray example. Absent the outlier, the average value is more accurate. This illustrates the weakness of a median combine: it is always going to be one of the values in the set. An average yields a value that is closer to the truth.

As a result, a median combine will have noticeably poorer signal to noise ratio (S/N) when compared to an average combine. So we appear to be stuck in an uncomfortable position. If we average combine, we have the best possible S/N but we retain the outliers. If we median combine, we get rid of the outliers but we have a poorer S/N.

What is an imager to do about all this? Isn't there some kind of compromise available?

Statistical (Data Rejection) Combine Methods

Given that noise is a key concept of statistical analysis, it should not be a major shock to learn that statistics can come to the rescue of the imager in search of the best combination of S/N and outlier removal.

In fact, a little thought experiment shows a simple way to achieve a combination of both effects. You could arrange the values in order, throw away the most extreme values, and then average what's left.

This is called min/max clip, and it's just one example of what can be done to combine images in a way that is both mathematically sound (higher S/N) and visually appealing (outlier removal).

As we move beyond a simple min/max clip, however, we get into more sophisticated mathematics. A few of the main-

stream image processing programs (e.g., CCDStack, MaxIm DL and Mira AP) include statistical combine methods.

The nature, features, and availability of such software changes with time. Please visit the New Astronomy Press web site for links to information related to this and our other books.

http://www.newastro.com/

Also visit the New Astronomy Press Yahoo group at:

http://groups.yahoo.com/group/ccd-newastro/

NOTE: Another way to look at this problem is to separate image combination from data rejection. Tools like CCDStack are starting to arrive on the scene. Such tools allow you to evaluate the parameters used for data rejection in the most useful way possible: visually. Visit the CCDWare web site for more information on CCDStack.

Unreliable Pixels

In addition to the outliers mentioned above, there is another type of problem that you can run into: unreliable pixels. These are pixels that allow a different amount of dark current at different times. In rare cases, unreliable pixels are an indication that the camera is not adjusted correctly at the factory, or that there is a problem with the camera firmware. But out-of-date dark frames are the most common cause.

If you take darks "by the book" and you still get large numbers of leftover hot and cold pixels, contact the camera manufacturer to get the problem fixed.

Despeckling (Hot/Cold Pixel Removal)

Even if you take and apply darks very carefully (and even if you use multiple darks to reduce random noise contribution from the darks), you will still wind up with at least a few pixels that are noticeably bright (hot pixels) or dark (cold pixels). Most camera control programs include despeckling tools to clean up these pixels.

Typically, such features incorporate "hot" or "cold" in the feature name. In CCDSoft you can use the *Repair* tool for hot and cold pixel removal. In MaxIm DL, use the *Dead Pixel* and *Hot Pixel* radio buttons in the *Kernel Filters* dialog (access via the *Filter»Kernel Filters...* menu item).

My general procedure is to take lots of light images, lots of darks, apply the darks to the light images, and then apply a moderate hot and cold pixel removal. This must be done on individual images. Combined images average values and smear the hot and cold pixels. It is especially important to do hot and cold pixel removal before aligning images, since alignment is guaranteed to smear the hot and cold pixels.

If you find leftover hot and cold pixels in Photoshop®, use the Dust & Scratches tool to remove them. Unlike the hot and cold pixel filters found in most camera control programs, the Dust & Scratches filter can be tuned to handle multi-pixel hot and cold spots. Increase the Radius setting to do this, but keep an eye on the smallest stars—they might get removed as well! Try lowering the Threshold setting instead, unless your hot and cold artifacts are simply so large they demand a radius setting larger than 1.

Master Reduction Frames

Just as you make a master luminance or color image, you should also make master reduction frames (dark, bias, flatfield). The noise that you can see so clearly in the light frames are also present (invisibly) in reduction frames. Taking lots of frames and combining them is just as effective at noise reduction in reduction frames as it is in light frames.

If you are seriously looking for both convenience and low noise in your images, consider building a rotating library of reduction frames. Take at least 8–10 reduction frames for each exposure time, bin mode, and temperature (not necessarily on one night!). Then take 8–10 more on subsequent nights, so that at any time you have at least 20–30 frames in your masters. As you take new frames, eliminate the old ones and make new masters using only the most recent frames.

The useful lifetime of library frames varies enormously. For some cameras, taking new frames nightly is essential. For others, new frames once a week will be fine. The only way to know what your camera can deliver is to test it. If you start seeing excessive hot and cold pixels, it's time to throw out the oldest frames and add some new ones.

Frame Types

Reduction frames come in three types: bias, dark, and flatfield. Darks are always needed (except for cameras that have especially low dark current), while bias frames are required only when scaling darks. Flat-field frames might or might not be required, depending on the factors described below.

Bias Frames

Bias frames record the starting pixel levels for your camera. A bias is an offset, and every pixel starts with a unique offset from zero. The bias frame records this offset for every pixel.

The only time to use bias frames is when you are scaling darks. You must scale darks when the exposure time of your dark frames does not match your light frames. You will get higher noise levels when you scale darks, but you will minimize this if you use bias frames. If you don't use bias frames, and you scale darks, you will be scaling the bias as well as the dark! This leads to excessive hot and cold pixels.

⭐ Tip: Always scale darks from longer to shorter. Don't try to scale a 3-minute dark to a 10-minute light frame. Scaling also scales noise, and scaling to a longer light exposure increases the noise contribution of the dark frame.

⭐ Tip: If you are taking short-exposure flat-field frames, you should still subtract a master bias even if you do not use darks. Short-exposure flats have so much signal that a dark might be unnecessary. But a bias frame will do the same basic thing for flats that it does for darks: allow the flat to scale properly when applied to light frames.

Dark Frames

Dark frames record the dark current that occurs during the exposure. If bias frames record the initial pixel state, then dark frames record the final pixel state. That is why scaling works: if you subtract the initial state from the final state, you get the exact record of what happened during the exposure.

Unless you have a camera that uses a special low-dark-current Sony HAD chip, you will be using darks to remove dark current from light frames. This is a straightforward subtraction if and only if the dark frame's exposure time and temperature match the light frame. See the earlier section on bias frames for a discussion on scaling darks.

Flat-Field Frames

Whereas bias and dark frames record electronic system noise, the flat field records the optical "noise" in your system. This can come from dust on optical surfaces, vignetting, etc.

General Technique

Unlike bias and dark frames, flat-field frames require skill and experience to do well. As it turns out, the hardest part of taking flats is the part of the process from which the flat field takes its name: flat (that is, even) illumination of the field. If you can master this part, you will have solved the main problem in taking good flats. Even illumination is easiest with twilight flats because the sky is evenly illuminated if you point your telescope near the zenith. Artificial illumination of the field (e.g., a light box) is trickier and requires patience and good detective skills.

I often get asked if a flat field is a good one. Unfortunately, you can't easily judge a flat just by looking at it. A flat might look odd but still do a great job. Ultimately, the only truly reliable way to test a flat field is to apply it to your images.

Note: Beware of the effects of light pollution gradients on your images and your flats. If you take sky flats, and you have light pollution gradients, you will need to subtract the gradient from the flat in order to get good results. Likewise, if your images have light pollution gradients, a good flat will not cure that. You'll still need to remove the gradients from the images separately from the flat process.

Overcoming Problems in Flats

In addition to the common problem of an unevenly illuminated field, there are other types of problems that can crop up. If you take flats during the day, you might wind up with light coming in where it shouldn't. For example, if light enters through even a tiny opening in the focuser tube, you could wind up with bright dust motes instead of shadows.

You might also find yourself dealing with surprisingly subtle uneven illumination of the field when taking flats. Moonlight filtered through tree branches, for example, can cause problems even though visually it doesn't seem like much of an effect. Even very small differences in illumination can mess up your flats.

Also keep an eye on your exposure times when taking flats. Very short exposure times (under 1–2 seconds) might introduce shutter artifacts into the flat. Any uneven illumination that results from shutter movement will be magnified by such short exposures. I recommend exposure times of at least a few seconds to avoid this problem.

As with all frame types, take as many flat-field frames as practical. If you are taking sky flats, you might have residual stars in the images. Use a statistical combine method to effectively remove all traces of stars from the master flat.

Image Alignment

If you are following my earlier advice and dithering your images (small shifts of a few pixels in both X and Y between images), image alignment is a critical step. It might seem to be a simple thing to align images, but in fact it's an area where making the right software choices can make a substantial difference.

A poor choice in alignment methods can increase the diameter of your stars. The best combine tools are made specifically for astro imaging. Conventional alignment tools are not concerned with stars, but with more typical landscape and portrait photography issues. For this reason, I strongly suggest that you limit yourself to using alignment tools that were specifically designed with astronomical imaging in mind.

Alignment Tools and Methods

One alignment tool stands out from the rest in terms of accuracy: Registar. Unfortunately, it also stands out in another way: the user interface is very awkward to learn and use. As a result, I tend to use Registar only when other alignment tools lack the sophistication to deal with a problem. For routine alignment tasks, any of the commonly used camera control programs have very good capabilities.

One camera control program, Mira AP, has better than average alignment capabilities. The interface isn't as challenging as Registar, but it still takes a little time to learn and use. The accuracy and flexibility of Mira's alignment tools make it a very worthwhile choice. It's more expensive, and less friendly, than the other camera control programs so I generally recommend it for intermediate to advanced users who want more sophisticated options for their image processing requirements.

Photoshop® isn't the ideal alignment tool, but it works. Photoshop® doesn't allow sub-pixel alignment, something that most astro-specific alignment tools offer. You can get around this by enlarging the image, aligning, and then reducing to original size. A 400% enlargement allows quarter-pixel accuracy.

Basic Histogram Processing

If you have done everything else right—dark frames, hot and cold pixel removal, noise reduction, and so on—histogram processing is much more successful because the noise is as low as it can (and should) be.

Histogram processing is like a reverse game of Hide and Seek. Noise is "it" and the goal is to seek out the noise, identify it, and then do everything you can to hide it!

In simplest terms, histogram processing should reveal everything in the image except the noise. The lower the noise level, the more you can bring out in the image. This all goes back to the underlying nature of noise—uncertainty incarnate. You cannot reveal things in the image that are uncertain. The better your S/N, the more details you can reveal.

The good news is that if you really sweat the details on gathering and reducing data, image processing gets easier.

Histogram processing involves expanding the dim portions of the image and compressing the bright portions. Expansion of the dim data is limited only by the noise. Compression of the bright portion is limited by your perception of what's important in the image.

Expansion and compression both involve allocation of the available brightness levels. There are only 256 brightness levels for you to use in presenting your data. You typically start out with about 65,000 brightness levels in the raw CCD data. So big changes are needed to pull this off. It's not simple or easy to stuff 65,000 values into 256 values.

Why 256 values? It starts with the eye, which really can't see more than about 200–250 brightness levels. Computer monitors and printers sometimes can't handle all of those 256 levels. If you ever felt that image processing was a challenge, finding out that you have to go from 65,536 (2^{16} and thus 16-bit) to 256 (2^8, or 8-bit) brightness levels tells you why it feels that way.

There are two ways to make this Big Transition. First, if all 65,536 levels don't have data in them, you can throw away the unused portions. For example, if you are imaging with a hydrogen-alpha filter, your brightest pixel values might be only 10,000 or 30,000. While the job is still huge, it's less than half the problem you face when going from 65,536 to 256. Similarly, if your image's background level is at 3,000, there's no point whatsoever in retaining those first 3,000 brightness levels. They are unused.

This first step—removing unused brightness levels—is done with the Photoshop® Levels tool. Unlike camera control programs, when you set the black and white points in Photoshop®, the data outside these points is discarded.

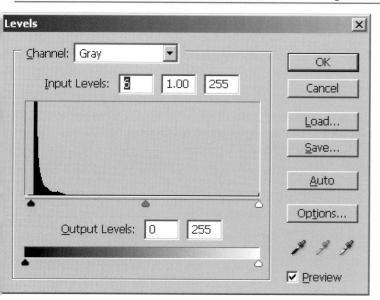

side of the histogram. Set the initial black point a bit to the left of the main peak in the histogram. Don't set it too close, or you might clip some useful data.

The example Levels dialog at top left shows a correct placement of the initial black point (a value of 6 out of 256).

Set Initial White Point

For many images, no initial white point setting is required. Set an initial white point only if the brightest value in the image is less than the maximum. The example below shows a histogram where the brightest value is around 243 out of 256 (in 16-bit brightness levels, this is approximately 243 * 256, or 62,208). The data is only a thin line to the right of the peak, but it is there!

Levels

Levels and Curves form the backbone of Photoshop® processing. Levels is where you can set three things about an image: the black point, the white point, and gamma.

NOTE: Photoshop® maps the 65,536 brightness levels in your 16-bit image into 256 slots when working in Levels (and in Curves). Remember to mentally adjust for the difference.

Set Initial Black Point

As you process the image, you will be expanding the dim portions of the image and compressing the bright portions. As you expand the dim stuff, the location of the black point can be seen with better and better precision. The initial black point should be set only if there is an obvious gap at the left

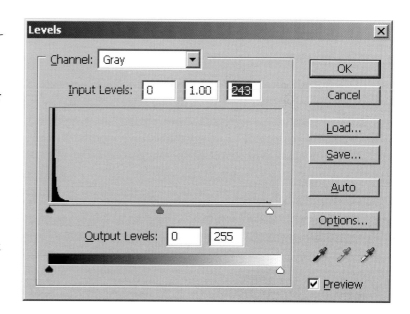

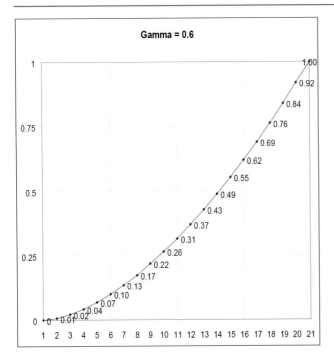

In the Gamma = 2.0 example, you can see that it generates something like a Standard Curve. However, there are some important differences. The Gamma-generated curve is more aggressive at the start, has a much broader Middle Zone transition, and not quite flat-to-the-finish. I do not recommend using Gamma adjustments in place of the Standard Curve.

Curves

Curves are non-linear transformations. Unlike gamma, which is a simple curve, you can use Curves to make very complex adjustments to the image.

Setting Gamma

The Gamma setting is located in the Levels dialog, but it's really a kind of curve. The graphs on this page plot the transfer curves for gamma settings of 0.6 and 2.0 as if the Curves dialog were being used. The gamma setting you enter is used as an exponent on the data values. This generates a positive or negative curve to brighten or darken the image.

Gamma can be useful for trivial brightening or darkening. If you do use it, values less than 1.0 darken and values larger than 1.0 brighten. Most of the time, I suggest that you use Curves which provides greater control.

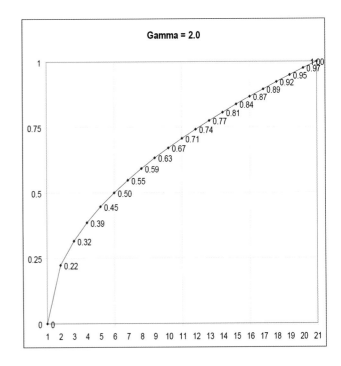

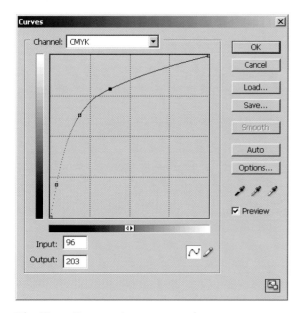

The Zone System gives you two key concepts you can use to control what is happening with Curves. There are several examples in chapters 2 and 3, but it's worthwhile to break Curves down into its component parts.

Rule #1: Use the Standard Curve

The dialog above shows a typical example of the Standard Curve. It's not important that you get the Standard Curve to exactly match this example. What is important is that the curve have a steep rise, a smooth turn, and then flat-to-the-finish (upper right portion of the curve). The steep rise expands the Dim zone. The smooth turn preserves the Middle Zone. And the flat finish compresses the Bright Zone without destroying the data in that zone.

Rule #2: Reduce aggressiveness as you iterate

It is typical to use multiple iterations of the Curves tool with the Standard Curve. You will almost always use a more aggressive Standard Curve to start, and then progressively less aggressive curves as you work on the image.

The steeper the initial rise, the more aggressive the curve is. If you are just starting out, you can begin with a less aggressive curve, and continue to use even less aggressive curves as you process. This approach will require more iterations, but that isn't going to change the results. It might even allow you to be more precise in your adjustments.

Make sure to use Levels to refine the black point location after every application of Curves.

Breaking Down the Curve

The three points on the standard curve correspond to specific Zones. You can control the appearance of each zone using the points on the Curve. Initially, you simply want a point that roughly corresponds to each zone. Later, during tweaking, you can use zonal (and sub-zonal) points more precisely.

Dim Zone Point

This is the point at far left. It defines the brightness and amount of stretch that occurs in the Dim Zone. The Dim Zone is the one that gets the most expansion, so it is no surprise that this is usually the steepest part of the curve. As you iterate through Curves, you will eventually reach a point where you can identify the Dim Zone very accurately. While using the Standard Curve, the horizontal position of the Dim Zone point should be located somewhere in the first half of the first quadrant, as shown.

Middle Zone Point

This is where the curve makes its turn. This is a transition zone between the expansion of the Dim Zone and the compression of the Bright Zone. The Middle Zone gets the least processing, and the positioning of its point on the curve reflects this approach. The idea in the Middle Zone is to do no harm to the data, just preserve what is already there. You can accomplish this by avoiding an unnecessarily abrupt turn.

Control Points (as Needed)

The control point (when needed to avoid clipping or to establish a flat-to-the-finish slope) compresses the bright data cleanly. This allows details in bright areas to remain visible while still allowing for appropriate compression.

Rule #3: Iterate!

Don't try to do too much with a single use of Curves. You can be more precise, and have greater control, when you do only what you can handle in a given iteration of curves.

Sometimes the image starts out very dark, with just a few stars (if that) visible. Don't be concerned about blind use of curves in this situation. As long as you apply some variation of the Standard Curve, the image will come out OK. Once you can see the data, you can modify the Standard Curve's aggressiveness to match the data and your preferences.

Advanced Histogram Processing

Multiple applications of the standard curve will only take you so far. At some point, you need to vary the shape of the curve to fit the requirements of the data or your preferences.

Identifying the Brightness Level of the Dim Zone

The Standard Curve will only take you so far. In fact, I expect someone to come up with a plug-in for Photoshop® or one of the camera-control programs that will automate the process of applying the Standard Curve. It is, after all, standard!

The image is in an interesting state after you finish applying several iterations of the Standard Curve. Prior to this point, the image is in a relative state—it doesn't matter what Standard Curve you use, just so long as the curve meets the requirements.

❧ Tɪᴘ: Always remember to complete the iterative Curves with an application of Levels. Always put the black point just to the left of the main peak.

The last application of Levels puts the image into an absolute state. You know exactly where the zones are located on the curve. You can take advantage of this state to establish an absolute value for the brightness of the dimmest salvageable details.

In fact, you can make a solid case that all of the processing so far had one objective: to expand the number of brightness levels available to the Dim Zone so that you can clearly see the base of the Dim Zone. This one feature is very important.

Once you know what brightness level corresponds to the base of the Dim Zone, that becomes your launching point for all further processing of the image. I guess you could call this one point the Turning Point. Everything before this has been relative and generalized. Everything after it is absolute and specific, zone by zone.

What you are determining is the Input value for this point. You can then set an Output value with Curves. This establishes the visual brightness of the dimmest available details. You can then set the brightness of the other zones. If you make the dimmest details too bright, you can use the History palette to go back and try a lower value for the Output value in Curves. Likewise, if you don't boost the Dim Zone enough, you can try a larger Output value.

The image at lower left shows how to find the dimmest usable details. They are defined by the S/N ratio. The dimmest details will be noisy, but they will contain some real, visible details. The Dark Zone lies below the brightness level of these details. If you are unsure if the detail is real, by definition it is in the Dark Zone. Look for something a little brighter.

In this example, I am using Curves to do a temporary (and very aggressive) stretch. This reveals the Dim Zone with great clarity. It is easy to find a dim detail that defines the base of the Dim Zone. The cursor, which has an eyedropper shape in Curves, is at upper right in the image. There is an enlarged view in the figure at upper right on this page.

The red arrow points to a very dim detail. It is noisy, but salvageable—the very definition of the Dim Zone. The blue arrow points to pixels that are in the Dark Zone. The S/N is lower, and there is no detail visible in pixels that are in that brightness range.

As a last check to see if this detail is representative of the Dim Zone, look for other dim details and verify that they have a similar brightness level. (The brightness level shows up in the Input box of Curves.)

See *Setting the Brightness of Dimmest Details* in chapter 3 for a complete step-by-step example.

Zonal Adjustments with Curves

When you have completed several iterations of the Standard Curve, the image more or less looks done, but it's not really *done*. What remains are decisions about how to distribute those 256 available brightness levels among the zones (and sub-zones once you get enough experience).

The Dark Zone is easy: you are trying to get rid of it, and you can do that with the correct black point (put it at the left edge of the main histogram peak). Getting the other zones distributed correctly calls for trade-offs and decisions about what is most important to you in the image.

The process starts with locating the brightness level of the dimmest details in the image, as described in the previous section. The figure above illustrates one approach to zonal (and sub-zonal) adjustments with Curves. The idea was to show core details while retaining detail in the arms.

From left to right, each point on the curve shown in the facing page does a specific job:

1. This is the most critical point. It defines the brightness of the dimmest useful Dim Zone details. Use the method from the previous section to find these details, then control-click to put this point on the curve. You can also note the Input value that corresponds to the identified portion of the image, and manually adjust the Input value of an arbitrary point. In this case, the dimmest details have a value of 10. Move the point vertically (or type in an Output value) to establish the desired brightness. Since the goal is to emphasize core and arm details, the Dim Zone is not brightened very much in this example.

2. This point corresponds to the start of the Middle Zone. In this example, the dominant arms of the galaxy are in the middle zone, so I moved this point up quite a bit to emphasize this portion of the Middle Zone.

❧ TIP: You can make trade-offs between the zones by raising and lowering the points vertically. To give more emphasis to the Dim Zone, for example, raise the first point and lower the second point.

3. This point is near the top of the Middle Zone, and represents spiral arms that are closer to the core of the galaxy. This is an example of sub-zonal adjustment. To keep these arms brighter than the arms further out (point #2), I also had to raise this point vertically by a significant amount. The effect of points #2–3, taken together, is to "spend" a large portion of the available 256 brightness levels on the Middle Zone.

4. This point corresponds roughly to the start of the Bright Zone. Because this is not a Standard Curve, I am free to do my transitional curve in the Bright Zone instead of in the Middle Zone. This is a moderately sharp turn so as to retain a reasonable number of brightness slots for the Bright Zone so we can see details near the core. I did not want to "waste" brightness levels on making a very slow turn. Try a gentler turn to see how it pushes the flat-to-the-finish portion up really high, close to clipping.

5. This final point is a control point, providing the flat-to-the-finish portion of the curve. This preserves as much detail in the Bright Zone as those aggressive Middle Zone adjustments will allow. This allows us to see most of the detail in the core area of the image.

You'll notice that I described moving all points vertically only. If you move the point horizontally, you can wind up switching zones unintentionally. Stick to vertical movements so that the zone you've identified (by control-clicking or visual inspection) is the zone you are adjusting.

You can of course make horizontal adjustments to points on the curve. Horizontal adjustments will adjust the contrast of the image by altering the slope of the curve between points. You can reduce contrast between points by moving them further apart. You can increase contrast by moving points closer together. However, moving points leftward generally increases contrast (it is compressing the dim part of the curve).

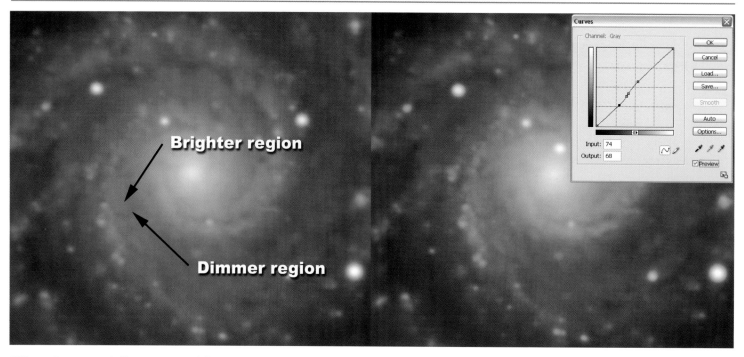

Micro-Contrast Adjustments with Curves

One of the more interesting possibilities with Curves is micro-contrast adjustments. This allows you to isolate a specific small range of brightness levels and to increase the contrast in this small range.

For example, if there is a dust lane in a galaxy, or a shock front in a nebula, you can use micro-contrast to make such features more visible by increasing the contrast between the feature and its surroundings. This works for dim and bright features.

The shape of a typical micro-contrast curve is shown at the top right of this page. To create a micro-contrast curve:

1. Control-click on the dimmer region. This places a point on the curve that corresponds to the brightness level in the region.

2. Control-click on the brighter region, which places a second point on the curve.

3. Use the Input and Output boxes to adjust the output values for each point. Increase the brighter output value and decrease the dimmer output value. The amount of the change should vary from 1 to 5 depending on how close the two points are on the curve. The further apart they are, the larger the change can be.

4. If the points are very close together, or if the change is large, you will get noticeable bending of the curve above and below the micro-contrast adjustment. To prevent the micro-contrast adjustment from ruining the overall tonal balance of the image, use control points as shown to flatten out the upper and lower portions of the curve.

5. Observe the result. It will affect all areas of the image with these brightness levels, so keep an eye out for unexpected side effects. Accept or cancel the changes.

In this example, you might or might not be able to make out the contrast between the brighter and dimmer regions (based on ink used, printer contrast, etc.) but that is the point! Even if the amount of contrast between two features is extremely limited, you can use a micro-contrast adjustment to increase the contrast and make the features visible.

Depending on your skill and the nature of the image, an image can tolerate about 3–10 micro-contrast adjustments.

Tweaking Curves for Final Appearance

Final tweaks can be made with a curve that looks like a much less aggressive version of the type of curve used for Zonal Adjustments. In most cases, the purpose of the final Curves tweaking is to refine the balance between the zones.

As always, if you don't like the final result, use the History palette to undo back to an earlier point. It is not uncommon for me to completely process an image, and then start over from the beginning using the lessons I've learned to do a better job the second (or third) time around.

☙ TIP: Use a large number of history states (I like 80 or 100) to give yourself lots of wiggle room. Use the *Edit»Preferences »General* menu item to change the number of history states.

Final background Level with Levels

At the risk of repeating myself too much, I'll say it again: always check the black point in Levels every time you use Curves. You might find that the last Levels adjustments means another trip back to Curves. That is a good thing! As long as your black point is still being adjusted, histogram adjustments might not be complete.

If the black point is too high, you are wasting some of those 256 slots. That means that contrast in the overall image is reduced, yielding a flatter-looking image. Given that the job is to reduce 65,536 brightness levels to just 256 levels, every one of those 256 levels counts.

If you are not using a calibrated monitor, you can snug the black point right up to the left edge of the main histogram peak. (In fact, you can sometimes go a bit further to the right than this if there are subtle gradients, but that's risky without a calibrated monitor showing you what you are doing.)

Sharing your images

So far we have been talking about getting the image to a point where it looks good on your monitor. That is only part of the battle. If you want to print it, or put it on the web, you run into a sad but true fact: the color and brightness settings of monitors and printers are all over the map. Not only are your monitor and printer settings probably quite different; there are also huge differences among monitors, and among printers as well.

The tool for dealing with this is color calibration (and it handles brightness as well as color).

Color calibration involves measuring the actual output of your monitor or printer, comparing that to a reference standard, and then developing a color profile that defines the output in a way that software like Photoshop® can understand. Color profiles are complicated and hard to understand at first, but they are so valuable, anyone who wants to share their images should be aware of what they offer and how they work.

Color Profiles

An entire book could be written about color profiles (and has been, several times!). But you don't need the skills of a professional to understand how to use color profiles. For example, if you have a recently-introduced printer, it probably comes with a default color profile. It won't be perfect, but it will be better than printing blind.

On the other hand, fewer monitors come with default profiles. And both monitors and printers can change their profile, at least in subtle ways, over time.

The good news is that you can purchase tools that will measure the characteristics of your monitor and/or printer (a process called calibration), and then create color profiles you can then use in programs like Photoshop®.

Some monitors come with their own calibration tools. I use a Sony Artisan because, although it's expensive, it's the best value out there (at least at the time of writing) in terms of price versus performance. La Cie also makes monitors that have their own calibration tools, but they are currently being sold separately so you have to know to ask for them.

You can also buy stand-alone calibration tools. The most well-known, and a very good choice, is the Pantone Spyder 2. It is available in several versions at various price points. (Pantone makes monitor-only, printer-only, and combined versions of the Spyder.) Bottom line: the more you pay, the more options you have.

Not every monitor can be calibrated, however. Some will have drifted in color or brightness so much that they cannot be adjusted enough to be calibrated—I've got one of these. Other monitors, especially inexpensive ones, might not even have adjustments for calibration. Older LCD monitors and laptops, in particular, lack calibration adjustments, but many CRTs do not have adequate calibration settings either.

The newer the monitor, the more likely it is to include calibration settings. You might not recognize the information in the specifications, so the best recourse is to ask in desktop publishing forums, or in the Yahoo group for this book.

❧ Tip: If you do not have calibration tools, you can fake it by printing out an image, observing any color or brightness problems, and then adjusting the image in Photoshop® to correct the output. The image might look horrible on your monitor, but if your goal is to print it out, this will get the job done (although at the cost of a lot of paper and ink). Make a note of the adjustments you make so it will go faster the next time. For example, if your printout is too green, use Color Balance to increase magenta in the image for printing.

Star Selection

There is a complete tutorial on star selection in chapter 5, so I'll just cover the key concepts here. The first key concept is the very idea of isolating the stars for processing. It is useful to think of the stars as a zone unto themselves. S/N is not the only way to define a zone; object-based zones work, too.

Stars have characteristics that are unique. This affects your processing choices—you would not do the same things to stars that you would do to a galaxy or a nebula.

Once you select stars, you can do all kinds of things to them. Generally, I recommend that you put them into a layer for separate processing. If you have minor touch-up to do, a selection alone might do the trick.

Stars are mostly part of the Bright Zone, but the dimmer stars in the image are in the Dim and Middle Zones. It can be useful to perform certain types of processing only on stars, and such processing crosses the traditional zones. This is where object zones come into play.

Not only can you treat stars as a zone, you can treat anything that has similar requirements as a zone. (Conversely, you can take two objects that are in the same zone and process them differently.) You could treat a planetary nebula as a zone for color balancing. Planetary nebulae have different color balancing requirements than the stars around them.

Putting Stars into One or More Layers

To put stars into a layer (where you can work on them in various ways), you first need to select them. The process is simple, but a little foreign the first time you try it. The process uses some of the more sophisticated features of Photoshop®, and the first time you work with these features you might feel out of your element. In addition to the list of steps that follows, you'll find detailed information about how all of these tools work in chapter 5.

1. Copy the background layer (Duplicate Layer)

2. Use the Dust & Scratches filter on the copy to remove stars. (Threshold=0, and just enough radius to do the job.)

3. Set the blend mode of the copy to Difference.

4. Use Color Range to select the stars.

5. Delete the copy layer

This leaves you with the stars selected in the original image. If necessary, manually select very large stars and remove any non-stars from the selection (e.g., bright knots in a galaxy or a shock front in a nebula). Save the selection in case you need it again later.

Manipulating the Star Selection

It's a good idea to save the raw star selection because it serves as a base for several different things you can do with the selection. The raw selection itself isn't ready to use. You need to modify it in various ways for various tasks.

The most common modifications to the star selection are expansion and feathering. Expansion adds a small amount of background to the star. This is useful for stuff like the Minimum filter (you need some background to fill in the area around the star when it shrinks, and to provide the input values needed by the minimum filter). Expansion also allows you to feather adequately, and to correct star elongation. So expansion is a routine part of star selection.

How much to expand depends on what you want to do. If you are going to make histogram changes to the stars (most commonly done to remove the faint halo from scattered light), you can make a reasonably large expansion (5–10 pixels). If you have stars in a wide range of diameters, you might want to take the time to break up the selection into multiple selections, each containing stars of a similar size.

⁂ Tip: It can be very useful to break up the star selection. Size isn't the only useful way to do it—the brightness of the background also makes a useful way to break up a star selection. For example, stars near the brighter portions of a nebula need different histogram processing than stars against the dim portions of the nebula.

⁂ Tip: A clever way to create a selection of just the larger stars is to contract the selection by a few pixels. This gets rid of the smallest stars in the selection. You can then expand again by the same amount before continuing. If you save this selection, you can subtract it from the original raw selection to yield just the smaller stars.

If you are going to sharpen the stars, a smaller expansion is called for. If the expansion is too large, you'll wind up with

dark circles around the stars from the sharpening. (You could use the Curves tool to correct this, however.)

The amount of feathering will also vary depending on what you are doing. I like to use a small amount of feathering, just a few pixels, when sharpening, to confine the sharpening. Smoothing works well with a larger feather size.

When you finish modifying the selection, right click on the layer in the Layers palette and choose New Layer via Copy. (In CS2, use the *Layer»New»Layer via Copy* menu item.)

Star Shape Corrections

One of the most useful things you can do with a star selection is to correct for elongated stars. It's very easy to do. Once you have the Stars layer, duplicate it. Set the blend mode of the copy to Darken. Then use the Offset filter to shift the copy to make the stars round. Use *Edit»Fade Offset* to make pseudo–sub-pixel adjustments.

The above technique handles linear problems, such as wind and guide errors. For non-linear problems, such as poor collimation, astigmatism, and so on, more complex techniques are required.

For astigmatism due to a color filter with non-parallel surfaces, you can resize the Darken layer by moving one edge so that the shift occurs most strongly near that edge.

For astigmatism in the corners due to not having a large enough flat field, you can copy just the corners into new layers and resize the Darken layer using the outermost corner.

The idea is to break the Darken layer into multiple layers, with one layer for each corner. Each layer must have the right extent to cover the elongation.

You can use nudging, offset, and resizing to correct any reasonable size of misshapen stars (where reasonable=2–3 pixels).

Zonal Sharpening

One of the main events that led to the creation of the Zone System was my observation that only certain parts of the image benefited from sharpening. Whenever I would try to use deconvolution, the problem was especially bad. The dim areas of the image would be horribly mangled even while the bright areas clearly could take more sharpening.

One thing led to another, and as I looked at the various portions of the image I could see that this was true for other types of processing as well. I could see a pattern emerging: the darker the feature, the worse it was for sharpening.

This is true, of course, because the signal to noise ratio (S/N) correlates with brightness. A dim area has low signal, and a bright area has lots of signal. In fact, I could easily rename the zones from Dark, Dim, Middle, and Bright to Fatally Noisy; Noisy but Salvageable; Moderately Noisy; and Low Noise.

Dark Zone: No Sharpening

The Dark Zone is officially bad data, and is eliminated (or very nearly so) in the final presentation. So no sharpening occurs here. If you did sharpen the Dark Zone, you'd get bad artifacts (you are sharpening noise, not data).

Dim Zone: Large-Feature Sharpening

The Dim Zone would not normally be a candidate for sharpening—the noise level is too high. But any sharpening technique that is noise-sensitive, or that at least avoids sharpening the noise, can be used in the Dim Zone. The large-feature sharpening technique, done with specific settings using the Unsharp Mask tool in Photoshop®, is one such option.

This technique is named for what it does: it sharpens only large-scale features in the image. It doesn't sharpen individual pixels with different brightness levels; it only works on areas of pixels. This reduces the artifacts from sharpening, allowing you to use this type of sharpening even in the Dim Zone.

The trick is simple: use a non-zero value for the Threshold setting. The larger the value, the less likely you are to wind up with artifacts. Of course, you also get less sharpening (only significant large-scale features are enhanced with Threshold values larger than about 2). This is very useful for enhancing dust lanes in galaxies and dim features in nebulae.

By definition, the Dim Zone is just too noisy for conventional sharpening techniques.

Middle Zone: Limited Sharpening

The brighter portions of the Middle Zone are sometimes good enough for limited sharpening. And if you can do large-feature sharpening in the Dim Zone, you can certainly do it in the Middle Zone. I typically use a smaller Threshold value for large-scale sharpening in the Middle Zone, so I am sharpening smaller features (because there is better S/N).

Bright Zone: Multiple Sharpening Options

The Bright Zone is where you can do the most aggressive sharpening. High S/N means that you are less likely to create artifacts when you are sharpening the Bright Zone. This is the area where you can make dramatic improvements in the details of the image with careful and appropriate sharpening.

I use Unsharp Mask in Photoshop® for most of my sharpening. It's a powerful and accurate tool. But if your S/N is high enough, you can also use deconvolution on the Bright Zone.

⁂ Tip: None of the currently available deconvolution tools work in Photoshop®. This means you can't use selections to limit the deconvolution area based on noise (though some programs will let you select a rectangle to deconvolve, and this will save you time but so will cropping before you deconvolve). You can put the deconvolved image into its own layer, and then blend the edges to match the original image. (Curves or a Gamma adjustment might be needed.) You can also grab the stars from a deconvolved image using the star selection techniques described in chapter 5. Use your imagination to combine various techniques and there's no limit to what you can achieve in the Bright Zone.

The key to success with deconvolution is to use it on images that have a very high S/N. The most common mistake is to try to deconvolve data that looks good—but isn't good enough for deconvolution. It takes a *lot* of signal to get good results from deconvolution. If you see noise artifacts even in the bright portion of the image after deconvolution, either you used settings that are too aggressive, or you simply do not have enough signal to benefit from deconvolution.

Cloning and Healing

Despite every effort, you will typically wind up with at least a few hot or cold pixels, or clusters of such pixels, that will only show up during histogram processing or sharpening. Just as histogram processing brings out faint details, it also reveals faintly hot and cold pixels that might not have been noticeable early in the process. You can use Photoshop®'s Clone Tool or Healing Brush to clean up such residue.

Clone or Heal? How to Choose

Both tools do nearly the same thing, but the Healing Brush preserves texture, and it is the better choice most of the time.

There is one situation where you should avoid the Healing Brush and use the Clone Tool instead. When you are working near a star, the Healing Brush has a tendency to pull the star's brightness into the result. This makes the healed area too bright. The Clone Tool, on the other hand, makes a literal copy of the source and is safe to use even right next to a star.

Star Sharpening

Once you have stars in a layer, you can do anything to the stars that you would do to any other layer or portion of an image. This includes sharpening.

Star sharpening is not without risks. If there are any obstacles in your optical path that create diffraction effects, those will get sharpened as well (especially on very bright stars). So you should limit the range of stars that are included. Determine what size of star you can safely sharpen by trial and error.

Another thing to be careful of is combining star sharpening with other techniques. For example, if you use a Minimum filter on the stars, adding sharpening on top of that might emphasize defects in the star, or create square stars. To use multiple techniques on stars, you really need superbly guided, extremely round stars as a starting point. Otherwise, minor defects get magnified when you mix sharpening techniques.

Types of Problems You Can Correct

Stars are ubiquitous in astronomical images, and they are the first things to show problems from guiding, collimation, focus, and other sources. In fact, you can learn a lot about what might have gone wrong in an image by studying the shapes and patterns of shapes in the stars.

Poor Focus (Soft Stars)

Nothing creates problems in an image faster than poor focus. And poor focus isn't something you can really correct effectively in processing. Sharpening can recover some of the lost detail, but not all. Unsharp mask will help a bit, but histogram changes are probably the best way to firm up out-of-focus stars. This is detailed in chapter 5.

Optical Quality Issues (Soft Stars)

Optics can limit the quality of focus. This typically shows up as soft stars. This becomes more of a problem as you get better at histogram processing. As you bring out more details in the dim areas, you also bring out more of the faint, scattered light around stars. This enlarges the stars' apparent diameter.

The minimum filter is the most effective tool for correction, though histogram techniques help somewhat. You are less likely to get good results from sharpening because of how soft the outer edge of the star usually is from this problem.

Bad Seeing (Fat Stars)

When the seeing gets bad, the stars get fat. There's no way around it! The effect is similar to what you see with optical quality issues (in effect, the atmosphere becomes a blurring lens). And the remedies are similar, though unlike scattered light, the effects of poor seeing tend to benefit a bit more from histogram techniques. (The edge isn't as soft.)

Consider Limitations of Star Sharpening

As I mentioned earlier, there are risks involved in star sharpening. For the most part, specific types of telescopes, or optical issues, can create subtle effects on stars that become much more obvious when you sharpen stars.

Enhances Diffraction Effects

If you have diffraction effects in your images, star sharpening will make them more noticeable. Depending on your tastes and the actual results you get, this might or might not be a problem. Diffraction effects range from large spikes from a secondary spider to ray-like patterns around bright stars from small imperfections in the tube or baffles of a refractor.

If you object to the artifacts, try histogram changes to the stars instead of sharpening.

Square Stars

Thick secondary spiders will create fairly heavy diffraction spikes. Applying sharpening could accentuate this, and create square-looking stars. The heavy spiders on Takahashi Epsilons are especially noted for this.

NOTE: Combining a Minimum Filter with sharpening can also create square stars.

Histogram Methods

Star sharpening isn't the only way to enhance stars. You can get a lot of improvement out of a simple histogram change using specially shaped curves. The sample curve in the image at right is typical. Point #1 is used to control the brightness of the small bit of background around the star relative to the image background. Keep the left end of the curve near a 45-degree line to prevent changes. This point will be higher on the curve for brighter backgrounds, and closer to the bottom left corner for darker backgrounds.

Point #2 controls the amount of shrinking of the stars. You might wind up using more than one point here. If you do, the lower one controls how much the star shrinks, and the upper one limits how much of the star can be affected.

Point #3 brightens the core of the stars, and maintains a reasonable brightness gradient across the stars.

If your telescope is prone to artifacts from star sharpening, stick to this histogram method instead of sharpening.

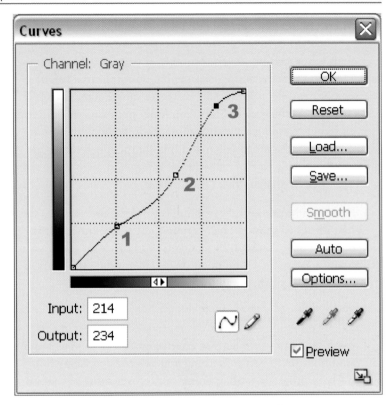

Unsharp Masking (Using Large-Feature Technique)

If you are going to sharpen stars, I suggest using a non-zero Threshold value in the Photoshop® Unsharp mask to do it. This avoids nasty little artifacts on the edges of stars (especially for the interline ABG cameras), and operates on the star as a whole instead of on pixel-to-pixel variations. The result will typically be noticeably smoother than conventional unsharp masking.

Deconvolution

If you have the long total exposure time required for good deconvolution (and thus very good signal to noise ratio), that is the best way to shrink your star sizes. (Interestingly, the star histogram method described on the previous page comes surprisingly close.) I use CCDSharp for most of my deconvolution; it seems to be the best of the lot in many respects. A new program from CCDWare, CCDStack, brings a new deconvolution tool to the table, however, and is well worth a look. Remember to use a very large number of iterations when working with high S/N data—you'll get superb results if you do. If you find that 2–4 iterations still leaves noise, then the image just isn't good enough for deconvolution.

Other deconvolution tools will sometimes be a better choice, but the unpredictable nature of deconvolution means you will need to use trial and error to find the ultimate for any particular image. This applies to the parameters you choose as well as to the tool you select in the first place.

Minimum Filter with Fade Option

Photoshop®'s Minimum filter is powerful, almost too powerful for many situations. It is a good tool, however, for dealing with unusually soft or large stars.

Make sure you eliminate the smallest stars from the selection or layer before you apply the Minimum tool. It can make the smallest star disappear! In nearly all situations, a radius of 1 will be more than enough for this filter. You will often need to use the *Edit»Fade Minimum* menu choice to avoid overly aggressive results.

Clean-Up for Dark Halos

Often, sharpening will leave dark halos around stars. Normally, this would be a reason not to sharpen so aggressively. However, if the stars are in a layer, you can clean up such halos using Curves. Make sure you only work on stars with a similar background brightness when you do this. Otherwise, you might fix some stars while making a mess of others.

You can also use the Dodge tool to manually brighten up such dark halos. This is almost always the better choice when working with selections instead of layers.

Zonal Smoothing

Just as sharpening has its zones, so does smoothing. Smoothing is for zones that have more noise relative to signal (that is, a low S/N).

Dark Zone: Heavy Smoothing

If you choose to retain portions of the Dark Zone after setting the Black Point, you should smooth these areas heavily. And I do mean heavily—the graininess in the Dark Zone is extreme, and a radius of 3 or more might be required to minimize the damage from leaving some of the Dark Zone in your image. You can also consider using third-party Photoshop® plug-ins designed for extreme smoothing.

Generally speaking, the best thing to do with the Dark Zone is to get rid of it by setting a black point high enough to hide this noisy, noisy area. You want to retain only enough of the Dark Zone to avoid a black background.

Dim Zone: *Appropriate Smoothing*

The Dim Zone is where you learn to master smoothing. Photoshop®'s Gaussian Blur handles the noise effectively. If you have version CS2 or later, the *Filter» Noise» Reduce Noise* menu item is the better choice. There are also some fancy smoothing tools out there—Grain Surgery and Neat Image, for example. Such tools are more complex to use, and might require more trial and error to come up with good settings. For Gaussian Blur, a radius of 0.3 to 1.2 pixels is effective. Use the lowest setting that yields good results.

⚜ Tip: The biggest risk in using the fancier tools is the temptation to smooth too much. Step back after smoothing and check if the result looks natural. If not, undo, and try with less aggressive settings. The Photoshop® CS2 Reduce Noise tool is one of the best-designed smoothing tools I've used. It gives you the settings you need to control over-smoothing, yet it can still be reasonably aggressive at smoothing serious noise.

Middle Zone: *Selective Smoothing*

The darker portions of the Middle Zone can often be improved with mild smoothing. Although I recommend doing minimal processing on the Middle Zone, the dimmest and brightest portions often benefit from processing normally applied to the Dim and Bright Zones.

For example, the dimmer portions of the Middle Zone can benefit from mild smoothing. A Gaussian Blur with a small radius, in the range of 0.3 to 0.5, is often effective at cleaning up mild graininess in this portion of the Middle Zone.

Bright Zone: *No Smoothing*

By its very nature, the Bright Zone doesn't need smoothing. The S/N is so high that grain is never in evidence in this zone. If you think you see grain in the Bright Zone, then it isn't the Bright Zone!

Photoshop® CS2 Reduce Noise Filter

This is one of the best reasons to upgrade to Photoshop® CS2 or later. The Reduce Noise filter (shown on facing page) is a superb noise reduction/smoothing tool.

It's not a miracle worker, however. Although it includes features to preserve details, you are still better off to select the Dim Zone with the Color Range tool before you use it. The Preserve Details feature works reasonably well across the zones, but the Sharpen Details feature behaves in very different ways in different zones.

In addition, if you select just the Dim Zone, you can use the Optimal Strength setting—a large one—for the noisiest parts of the image. You can go back and use Color Range to select just the Middle Zone, or maybe the noisiest parts of the Middle Zone, and use a smaller Strength value on that area.

The Preserve Details setting can be used to control how effectively dim stars are preserved. With a low setting, you will get a lot of undesirable blurring of dim stars. Use a value of 5–10 to keep those dim stars in good shape. This ability is one of the key reasons to use this tool rather than a simple Gaussian Blur. It is just about impossible to control the dimmest stars if a Gaussian blur of 0.8 or larger is needed.

The Reduce Color Noise feature is dimmed because in this example a luminance image is being smoothed. You can use this feature to control the smoothing of color noise in an RGB or LRGB image.

The Sharpen Details feature doesn't apply when smoothing with Reduce Noise in the Dim Zone. All you will sharpen will be the grain from the noise. If you use Reduce Noise on the Middle or Bright Zones, then you might find some benefit from a non-zero setting. Otherwise, you will do the least damage to your Dim Zone by leaving this set at zero.

The Remove JPG Artifacts feature can be useful if you import a JPG image to use as an RGB layer, adding color to a luminance image.

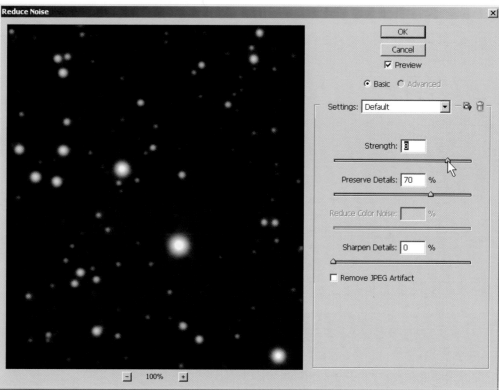

If you are working on a color image, the Advanced radio button will be active. If the noise levels are different in the color channels, you can use the Advanced mode which allows you to adjust the noise reduction in each color channel individually.

For example, if you have light pollution that is dominant in green, you will have more noise in green due to the additional shot noise. You can use a larger strength setting for the green channel to add extra noise reduction.

Image Processing: Color

Most, but not all, of the image processing you do on the color and luminance components of an LRGB image is done separately. That is, you process the luminance, then you process the color, then you combine them.

There will be at least some tweaking of both the color and the luminance layers after the combine. Photoshop® CS supports 16-bit layers, so you can do your tweaking and observe the effects in real time. In prior versions of Photoshop®, you had to make your changes, convert the images to 8 bits, combine and evaluate, and then start over again with the 16-bit data and try again if necessary.

≈ TIP: The fact that Photoshop® CS supports 16-bit layers means you can, if you wish, combine the raw luminance and color images and then work on them.

The histogram processing of the color layer is not substantially different from what you do on a luminance layer. When you are doing an LRGB combine, however, there are some things you need to do differently.

- The act of combining color and luminance yields a result that is slightly brighter than either component alone. Hold back a little on your histogram processing in both luminance and RGB layers until after the combine. You can then see the effects of histogram changes on each layer and decide exactly what you want to do.

- Changes to the color histogram affect color saturation. Up to a point, the more heavily you apply Curves to the color channel, the more saturated the colors will be. You can also control saturation using the Hue/Saturation dialog.

- If the total exposure time for the color layer is less than for the luminance, you will suffer loss of color saturation. You can compensate using the Hue/Saturation dialog, but you cannot create color where it is missing. You can either accept the weak color, or you can hold back on the luminance channel histogram processing in Curves to accommodate the weak color.

Color Binning Effects

It is common to bin the color images for an LRGB combine, and to capture the luminance data unbinned. There is sound logic behind this approach. The eye sees color at a lower resolution than brightness, so it makes sense to shoot the color data at a lower resolution. Even so, there are potential problems from this approach.

Nebulosity Issues

If the stars in your image are in front of nebulosity, you might see one of the primary problems with binned color. After resizing, the stars in the resized color image will typically be larger than the stars in the luminance image.

NOTE: If you are imaging with a long focal length and a small image scale, you might not see much difference between the sizes of the stars in the image with different bin modes after resizing. Better seeing usually reduces the impact from this problem as well.

When you combine binned color with unbinned luminance in an image with nebulosity, the brighter stars in the color image are larger than the corresponding stars in the luminance image. When the layers are overlapped, there is therefore no color in the area immediately around the stars.

The brighter and more colorful the nebula, the more likely it is that you will be unhappy with the results from binned color. It is usually the brightest nebulae—the Eagle, the Lagoon, etc.—that show this problem. You can take unbinned color in such cases, but you will need much longer exposures.

If you do your color binned, and the star sizes are too large for a good color combine, try a minimum filter on the stars as a selection. Use a larger than normal area of background around the star to help bring color inward.

Blur to Clean Up Color Noise

The key to success with color images is to take lots of them and combine into master red, green, and blue images. You can then make an RGB image out of the color masters. If you are using a one-shot color camera, the idea is similar—take lots of images and combine them to make a master RGB that is as low in noise as you can manage.

It should therefore come as no surprise that the most common problem encountered in color images, and in the color portion of LRGB images, is too much noise.

Just as the dim portions of a luminance image will be noisier than the bright portions, the dim portions of a color image will likewise be noisier. The consequence of color noise is weak, false, or missing color.

In addition, if the luminance image has significantly lower noise than the color images, you will either get pale colors if you fully process the luminance data, or you will need to hold back on the luminance data (be less aggressive with Curves).

In the RGB image below, color is weak. The main object has at least some color, but the background galaxies (several are enclosed in the red ellipse) have no color whatsoever.

A second consequence of severe color noise is false color. The graininess of noisy color translates into a patchwork of col-

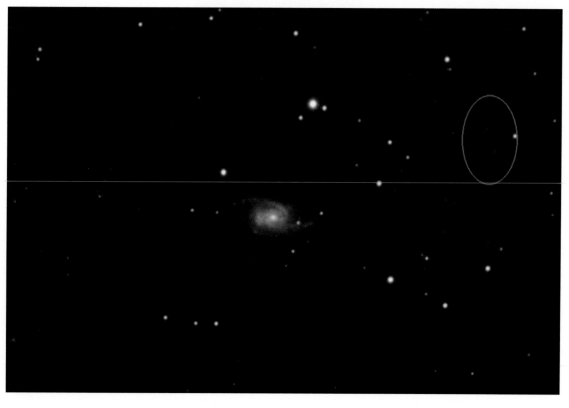

ored pixels—which looks pretty awful. The grain sometimes looks clumpy, giving color to things that don't have color, and it gives the wrong color to some areas of the image. The galaxy color in the image above is OK (not great), but the dim portions of the galaxy exhibit both noisy color and false color.

The cure for excessively noisy color data is to blur the RGB layer in an LRGB combine. There is a cost—blurring will reduce color saturation (make the color more pale). So use color blurring with care. When you do use it, you will typically need to blur fairly heavily to get rid of the graininess. This will wash out color entirely in the noisiest areas if done correctly, using the *Filter» Blur» Gaussian Blur...* menu item. A blur radius of 1.5 to 3.0 is typical. MaxIm DL has an effective tool called Color Smoothing which also reduces the color contrast.

If portions of the color image are noisy, and portions are reasonably crisp, then you can use zone-based selections to blur only the noisy stuff. This will be the Dim Zone of the color image. I recommend that you hide the color layer and use the Color Range tool to select the Dim Zone using the luminance layer. (The grainy color in the RGB data will make it a nightmare to get a clean selection.)

In the image below, the color noise is dramatically lower. Not only does the small galaxy have good color, but even the distant galaxies have clear, saturated color. Low noise wins again.

❧ Tip: If you are using a one-shot color camera, duplicate the color layer and desaturate the copy to get a luminance layer for making the selection. If you like, set the blend mode of this layer to Luminance instead of re-arranging the order of the layers.

In Photoshop® CS2, use the *Reduce Color Noise* setting in the *Filter» Noise» Reduce Noise* dialog to control color noise—one channel at a time if necessary.

Color Exposure Time

Color exposure time does not stand on its own. The length of color exposure time relative to luminance/clear exposure time is of critical importance. This ratio determines how saturated the color exposures will be. You can always hold back on processing the luminance image if the color data is too short (and thus noisy), but that is hardly optimal! I have established some general guidelines for color exposure times relative to luminance exposure times that will enable you to get the result you are looking for.

The bottom line on color exposure times is that progressively longer exposures yield color in progressively dimmer portions of the image. Let's say you are imaging M51. A very short color exposure relative to luminance will give you color in the bright portions of M51, but the dim areas of M51 will be pale or have no color at all because of the noise. Background galaxies might have a few spots of color, but it will be unreliable.

A longer color exposure will lend color to the dimmer areas of M51. The longer your color exposures, the richer the color will be. And of course if you double your luminance exposure time, you should double your color exposure time or the color will become pale. It is the relative noise levels in the two data sets, not the absolute level of noise, that determine how rich the color will be in an LRGB image.

Assuming that luminance is unbinned and color is binned 2x2, I would never take color exposures that are less than 25% of the luminance exposure. That's a minimum; to get some color in the dim areas of the image, color exposures that are 50% of the luminance exposure time is a better choice.

For really rich color, use equal time (or even more) for the color. The very best color images you've seen always use a large amount of color data relative to the luminance data. In fact, if you get enough color, you can boost the color saturation because there won't be much color noise to ruin the effect. Increasing saturation on noisy color data makes a royal mess because of the mixture of graininess in the color channels.

At some point, if your color data has low enough noise, you can boost saturation to get richer colors even if the relative color/luminance exposure times are not as good as I've suggested. The longer your exposure times for both sets of data, the more likely this will be true.

Unbinned Color Exposure Times

The question always comes up: what about shooting color unbinned? The better your seeing, the less likely it is that you will benefit significantly from unbinned color. This runs counter to intuition, but there is a reason for this statement. In better seeing conditions, you will normally see a smaller difference in star sizes between the binned and unbinned exposures. This leads to better blending of the two data sets into an LRGB exposure.

If seeing isn't good enough, then by all means feel free to take unbinned color exposures. But keep in mind that you'll need longer color exposure times to get good results. The goal of the color exposure time is to get the noise down in the color images. You can do this more easily with binned images because the read noise is much lower (you are reading out four pixels at once, so there is only one instance of read noise for four pixels). If you take unbinned images, make sure that you take individual exposures that are long enough to allow the shot noise to overcome the read noise by a wide margin. Otherwise, you will need to take double, triple, or even quadruple the exposure times unbinned to get a low enough noise level.

Binning versus not binning is therefore a trade-off. You gain resolution unbinned, but you also have higher noise levels to deal with. If you can't take long enough unbinned exposures to swamp the read noise, you might be better off with binned color exposures and expending some effort to tame the problems in the processing stage.

Color Balancing

Color balancing is a complex subject, but I'll hit some of the highlights here. You can work through a complete color balancing tutorial in chapter 6.

Color balancing is actually a multi-stage process. There are different ways that color can be out of balance. The typical stages in color balancing are bias removal (background color levels), color balancing (foreground), noise balancing (with luminance data and among color channels), and saturation adjustments.

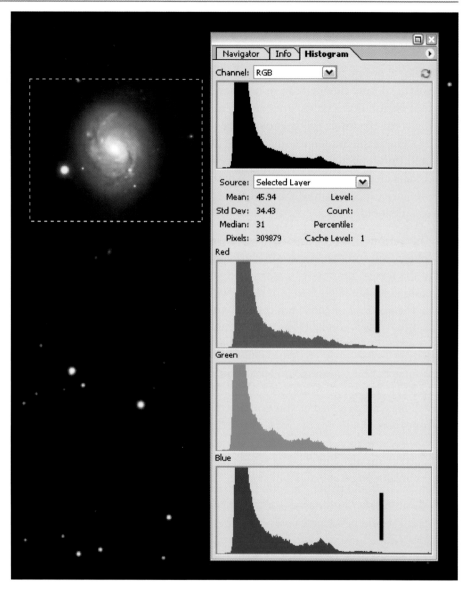

Background Color Balance

Background imbalance occurs when one or more colors have an offset histogram peak. This offset is called a bias (not the same thing as a bias frame at all!).

Correction is simple: adjust the black points of all three color channels so they are the same relative to the left side of the histogram peak. *Always* do this before a color balance!

❧ TIP: If you have a gradient in your image, clean up the gradient and then deal with color bias. A gradient creates a sloped left side of the histogram (or multiple peaks) and you cannot adjust black levels accurately until you clean up the gradient.

As with normal black point adjustments, you will need to refine the accuracy of the color channel black points interactively as you modify the combined histogram with curves.

❧ TIP: Changes to foreground color balance affect color bias. Just as you always adjust Levels after Curves, check your background levels when you adjust the foreground color balance.

Foreground Color Balance

I prefer to do most of my color balancing using Photoshop®'s Color Balance dialog. This dialog makes it very clear what is happening during balancing. You aren't just adding or subtracting a color. When you add green, you get less magenta. When you add cyan, you get less red, and so on.

It is common to have light pollution create a color bias (often in green). Removal of this bias will create a deficiency in the green channel. You can fix this in processing by moving the magenta/green slider to the right.

❧ TIP: A better way to deal with this problem is to take a few extra green exposures. When combined, this will lower the noise in the green channel, and provide better balance after color bias correction for the effects of light pollution.

You can use what I call the pseudo white point to make color balancing easier. The figure on the page at left shows the expanded, all-channel histogram view. I have added vertical bars to indicate where the pseudo white point is for each color channel.

Assuming that the subject of the image, M77, has an overall white color balance, the image has too little green and too much blue. You can correct this with the Color Balance tool: move the Yellow/Blue slider toward yellow, and the Magenta/Green slider toward green.

A word of caution is in order with respect to color bias. With some subjects, lining up the pseudo white points will do the job. But many objects have some intrinsic color. You can use the NASA Extragalactic Database (NED) to learn the relative magnitudes of many galaxies through various filters, and use this information to guide you in correcting color balance.

Equal Noise in Color Channels

It is common practice to use different exposure times through different filters in order to get balanced color. When you adjust the exposure times for each filter, what you are really doing is trying to get the same level of noise in each color. When the noise levels are the same, then the colors will balance automatically.

This is tricky. From an intuitive standpoint, it would seem that if you make something the same brightness level, you will get correct color balance. But what really happens if you achieve a given brightness level with different exposure times? And is exposure time really the only variable here?

It isn't just the exposure time that is different with different filters. The QE of the CCD chip varies with color as well as the amount of light passed by the filters. The sky glow might be different in different colors—the sky is often brighter in green or red from light pollution, for example. So adjusting exposure time for color balance in bright objects typically leaves different color bias levels in the color images. When this bias is subtracted, the color balance changes, too.

When you consider that the brightness of the sky in different colors also changes over time (for example, parking lot lights might be turned off at a certain hour), things really get complicated. It's just about impossible to take truly color-balanced images on any given night. The best you can hope to do is to get close, and then use image processing skills to clean up the color bias, and balance the color.

The cure for high noise is more data. Taking a few extra exposures in a noisy channel will lower the noise in that channel, and give you a better chance to correct the color balance during processing. You can also take longer exposures to compensate for the higher noise level. Of course, taking lots of color

images lowers the noise overall, and this is the best way to do it. Lower noise is always better!

Emphasizing Structural Details

Although color certainly makes for a good-looking image, there is a practical side as well. When you take long color exposures, subtle coloration suddenly becomes crystal clear. The image on the facing page is a monochrome image of a small part of the Rosette Nebula. You can make out some structural details based on brightness alone.

The areas of dust are very clear. They are dark, and you can easily interpret them as dust or molecular clouds or at the very least something that blocks the light from behind. There is an overall brightness to most of the image, with a few spots being brighter than the others. The question immediately comes to mind: What are those brighter areas, and how, really, are they different from the other bright areas?

This monochrome image just doesn't tell us much, does it?

Take a peek at the images on the following pages. Color makes a huge difference at both the emotional and scientific levels. Emotionally, the image now packs a heck of a wallop. It really hits you with a strong sense of "you are there." Scientifically, color adds an enormous amount of information to the image.

Ken Crawford made this image using emission-line filters, so that the light we see is emitted by very specific elements in the nebula. The light from these filters has been mapped into conventional colors. Hydrogen alpha, O[III], and SII have

been mapped into red, green, and blue. This tells us that those ethereal blue structures contain significant amounts of singly ionized sulfur.

Rosette Nebula detail, Ken Crawford—Monochrome version

Rosette Nebula detail, Ken Crawford - False color version
Red = Hydrogen Alpha
Green = [OIII] (doubly ionized oxygen)
Blue = SII (ionized sulfur)

Chapter 5

Selecting Stars

Selecting Stars

Objective

Select only the stars in the image so you can process them apart from the rest of the image.

Techniques
- Dust and Scratches filter
- Using a large radius on the Dust and Scratches filter
- Minimum Filter with fade
- Unsharp Mask with non-zero threshold value
- Color Range, adding to selected range

Tools
- Dust and Scratches filter
- Minimum Filter
- Unsharp Masking
- Color Range (Selection)

Description

To isolate the stars in the image, you will create a new layer, remove the stars, and then use the Difference blend mode to allow you to select what is different between this layer and the original image: the stars. Once you have a selection that contains the stars, you can:

- Save the selection
- Copy the stars into a layer
- Create multiple layers of stars based on brightness, size, background brightness, or other characteristics
- Change blend modes to alter the star shape (e.g., to fix elongation)
- Apply Curves or sharpening to the stars

Definitions

Hot pixels: Individual pixels that show up as white dots after data reduction. There are always slight variations in the pixels, but a small population of pixels on any CCD chip vary more than others. These are called, simply enough, the hot pixel population. They are typically just a few percent of the pixels. In any given image, part or all of the hot pixel population might yield bright pixels after data reduction. Remove using a despeckling, hot pixel, or Dust & Scratches filter.

Cold pixels: Similar to hot pixels, but in the other direction. These are pixels that show up as dark spots. Remove using a despeckling, hot pixel, or Dust & Scratches filter.

Minimum filter: A pixel-based filter that looks at the brightness of surrounding pixels, and then adjusts the brightness of a given pixel based on the minimum of the surrounding brightness values. Used on stars to shrink their size. Best applied to large/fat/out-of-focus stars because it will actually remove small stars.

Unsharp mask: A sharpening filter that subtracts a blurred (unsharp) version of the image (mask) in order to sharpen it.

Blend mode: A Photoshop® setting that allows you to merge data from more than one layer. When selecting stars, use the Difference blend mode.

Difference blend mode: Reveals the difference between two layers. When selecting stars, you first modify one layer to remove the stars. Applying the Difference blend mode to the upper layer then reveals only the stars so you can select them.

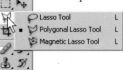

Fly-out menu: Many tools on the Photoshop® Tools palette have variants. For example, there are multiple Lasso tools, including the default *Lasso Tool* and the *Polygonal Lasso Tool*. To choose a variant that is not currently visible, click and hold on the current variant and a fly-out menu will appear as shown at left, allowing you to select the variant you want to use.

Dust & Scratches » Radius: This setting determines how aggressive the star removal will be. Always use the smallest practical radius. A too-large radius might cause nebulosity or parts of a galaxy to get selected.

Dust & Scratches » Threshold: This setting should always be set to zero when removing stars from a layer copy.

FWHM: Abbreviation for Full Width at Half Maximum. The width of a star image at half the maximum brightness level. Useful only on unsaturated stars. Most camera control programs include an easy way to measure FWHM.

Over sampling: Occurs when the image scale, expressed in arcseconds per pixel, is smaller than optimum. For example, if you are imaging at 0.33"/pixel, and your FWHM is 3.0", you are over sampled. Optimum sampling uses a FWHM about 2.8–3.4 times larger than your image scale.

Under sampling: Occurs when the image scale, expressed in arcseconds per pixel, is larger than optimum.

Photoshop® Tips

Dust and Scratches Filter

Filter » Noise » Dust & Scratches

It often happens that even after careful data reduction (aka calibration), you wind up with some hot and/or cold pixels in an image. The figure at right, a close-up of M27 enlarged to 200%, shows an extreme example of a hot-pixel problem.

Photoshop®'s Dust & Scratches filter is just one of many despeckling filters available for dealing with this type of problem. MaxIm DL, CCDSoft, Astroart, and most other CCD-specific software

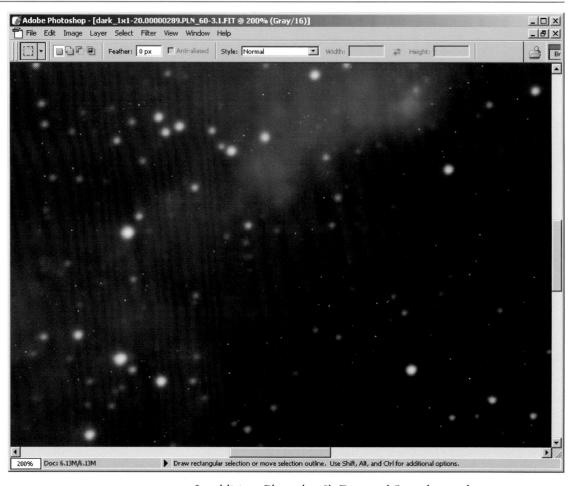

contain some form of hot and cold pixel removal. The nice thing about working with this problem in Photoshop® is that you can tune the despeckling to exactly the amount needed to solve the problem. Most other programs do not offer a preview mode.

In addition, Photoshop®'s Dust and Scratches tool removes both hot and cold pixels at the same time. You do not need to use separate tools for each type of problem.

❧ Tip: Cold pixels are often caused by hot pixels in dark frames. Cure this by combining a larger number of frames.

For hot and cold pixel removal, make sure that the Radius is set to 1. A larger radius will obliterate stars as well as hot and cold pixels.

❧ TIP: Depending on the size and severity of the hot pixels in your image, even a radius of 1 might result in some damage to the stars. Keep an eye on both the stars and the hot pixels to find a balance that gives you as much improvement as possible without undue damage to stars.

To find the sweet spot for hot and cold pixel removal, start with a relatively high Threshold value (e.g., 100), and lower it until you have removed the hot/cold pixels to your satisfaction. In this example, a threshold of 20 works well. This is a lower number than is typical, owing to the severity of the hot pixel problem. Typically, values from 20 to 40 will get rid of your hot pixels.

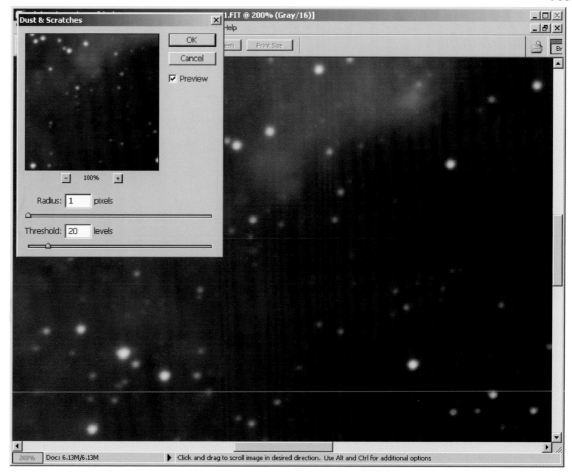

The above image shows the result of applying the Dust & Scratches filter to the image. Note that the hot pixels and other problems are almost completely cleaned up, and that there is virtually no change to the stars in the image.

Minimum Filter

Filter » Other » Minimum...

The Minimum filter compares the values of adjoining pixels and assigns a new value to each pixel based on the minimum value found. It spreads out dark areas, and reduces bright areas. When applied to stars, it tightens them up.

A good use for the minimum filter is reducing bloated stars. Bad seeing, poor focus, over sampling, or limited optical quality can result in stars that are larger than you want them to be.

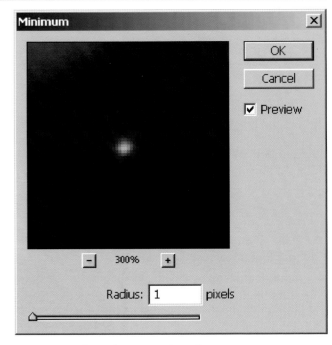

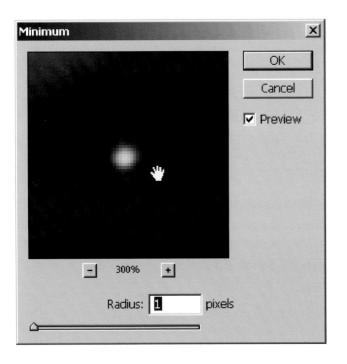

The images here are enlarged 300%. They show a Minimum filter with a radius of one pixel on a typical bloated star. Fractional values are not allowed.

Even with a radius of 1, the minimum filter might still be too heavy-handed for your images. (The Minimum filter also might make non-round stars worse; see chapter 8 for help with rounding up stars.) The solution is to use yet another cool Photoshop® tool: the Fade. Use the *Edit » Fade* menu item to bring up the Fade dialog, and choose a percentage between zero and 100 percent to determine how much of the Minimum filter to retain. For example, if you want three quarters of the Minimum filter effect, use a percentage of 75.

Unsharp Masking

Filter» Sharpen» Unsharp Mask...

The name of this tool is confusing—why unsharp an image, and what is masking anyway?

The name is misleading, but descriptive. Unsharp masking makes an unsharp version of the image (blurred, in other words), and then uses it as a mask to sharpen the image.

The Unsharp Mask tool finds pixels that differ from surrounding pixels and increases the contrast between them. The lighter pixels get lighter and the darker pixels get darker.

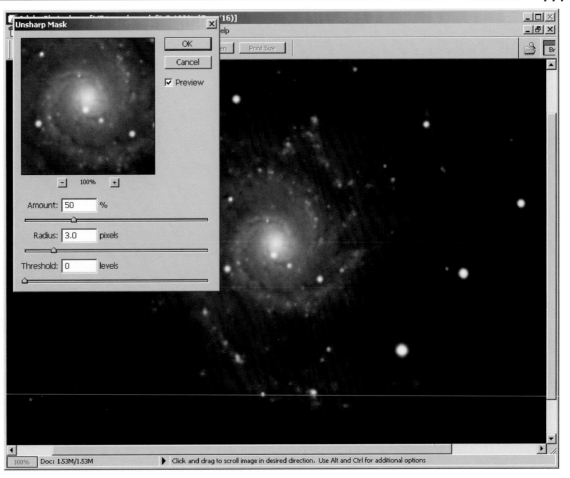

The threshold setting determines how much difference there must be before contrast is boosted, so a higher threshold setting will limit the sharpening to large-feature areas of the image. It will also make sure that sharpening is regional, not pixel-by-pixel. Non-zero threshold settings are ideal for things like galaxy dust lane enhancement.

The radius value determines the size of the region to which each pixel is compared. The greater the radius, the greater the increase in contrast, and the heavier the sharpening effect.

Color Range

Select» Color Range...

The Color Range tool allows you to select pixels based on brightness. Since brightness correlates strongly with noise, you can use this tool to select specific zones in the image.

If you are not using the latest version of Photoshop®, you must convert images to 8-bit color before you can use the Color Range tool. Photoshop® CS supports 16-bit color for many tools, including the Color Range tool, and this is a key reason to upgrade.

Set the Fuzziness to around 40. This will give you a workable fuzzy selection appropriate for most astro images. Use a smaller value whenever you need finer control over how much you are selecting. Set the Selection Preview to Quick Mask. This will show red for all unselected pixels.

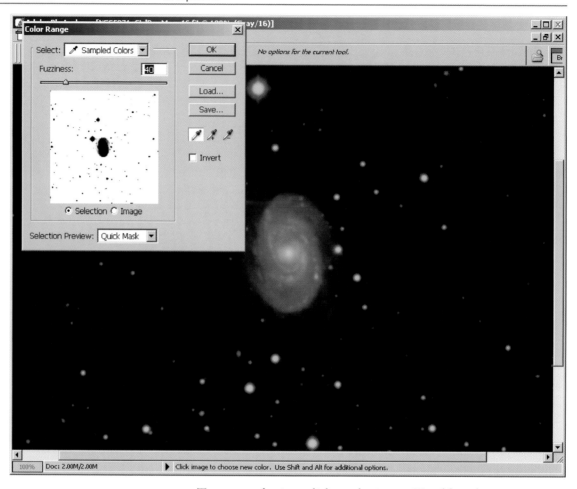

To start a selection, click on the image. To add to the area selected, click the middle eyedropper, then click on other brightness levels in the image. The above example shows a selection of the Dim Zone. When selecting the Dim Zone, keep clicking until you have selected all noisy areas, as above.

Tutorial Start

Open the File

If you would like to follow along with this exercise, open the following file from the DVD in Photoshop® CS (or later):

\C2\m74_final.fit

Duplicate the Layer

Make sure that the Layers palette is visible. You can open it with the *Window» Layers* menu item.

🖐 TIP: To display any palette, click on the Window menu and then click on the Palette name.

Right click on the name of the layer you want to duplicate. (It does not have to be the currently selected layer.) In a newly opened FITS image, there is only one layer. It has the default name of "Background." For this example, right click on that name.

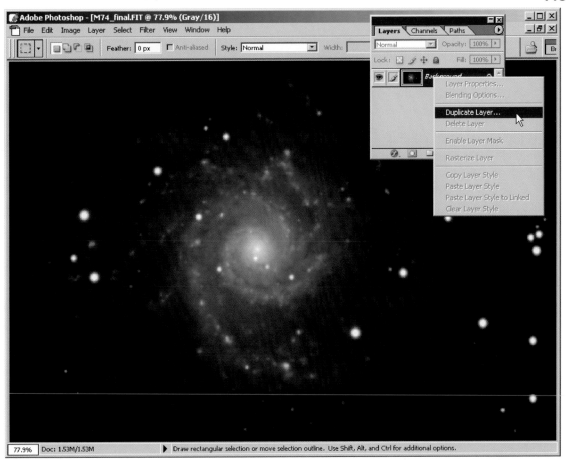

This displays a pop-up menu as shown above. Only one menu choice is active on the menu: *Duplicate layer.* Click on this menu choice.

🖐 TIP: Later versions of Photoshop® CS might show more options. Duplicate Layer can also be found on the Layer menu.

This opens the *Duplicate Layer* dialog, as shown at right. The default name of the new layer is **Back-ground copy.** You can accept this or change it, as you wish. You can change the layer name later using the *Layer»Layer Properties...* menu item.

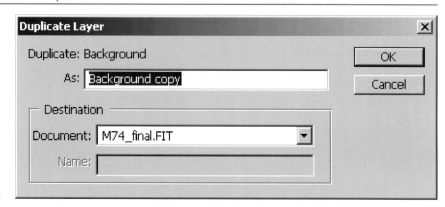

The default destination is the current document, which is where you want to have the duplicate created. (You can also duplicate a layer to another document by selecting the document from the drop-down list.) Click OK to duplicate the layer.

This adds a new layer to the Layers palette, with the name **Background copy.** The new layer is highlighted, indicating that it is the active layer. Two things tell you that this layer is active: there is a brush icon present, and the layer name is highlighted. At this point, both layers are identical.

➴ TIP: Click on a layer name to make it the active layer.

Remove the Stars

To access the Dust & Scratches dialog, use the Filter»Noise» Dust & Scratches menu item

The *Dust & Scratches* dialog (see figure on next page) displays a small preview area and two adjustments that you can make: *Radius* and *Threshold.* Both will default to the last used values. For star removal, set the threshold at zero and the radius at 5. Increase the radius setting until the stars are mostly gone. The larger stars will not disappear entirely; they will start to get darker and that is sufficient.

➴ TIP: If you were to increase the radius until the largest stars were completely gone, that would complicate the remaining steps of the exercise. The galaxy becomes more and more distorted as you increase the radius, and it becomes harder and harder to select only the stars. Use the smallest radius that will get the job done.

With a radius that is too large, you will change the galaxy so much that parts of the galaxy will wind up getting selected. If this happens, you can either start over, or deselect the galaxy portions manually. Use the Alt key with a selection tool to subtract from the selection.

You will develop a visual feel for what constitutes "too much" radius on galaxies and nebulae.

The figure at right shows the result of setting the radius to 7 and the threshold to zero. The smaller stars have already disappeared, but the brighter stars in the image are still present, largely unchanged.

Note that the galaxy itself is also changing as you apply the Dust & Scratches tool. Large radius values pretty much destroy nebula and galaxy details. (You won't be able to use radius values larger than 1 when you are applying the Dust and Scratches filter for hot and cold pixel removal.)

Continue increasing the radius value until the brightest stars begin to get darker. If there are no large, bright stars in the image, a lower radius setting will be sufficient to get the job done.

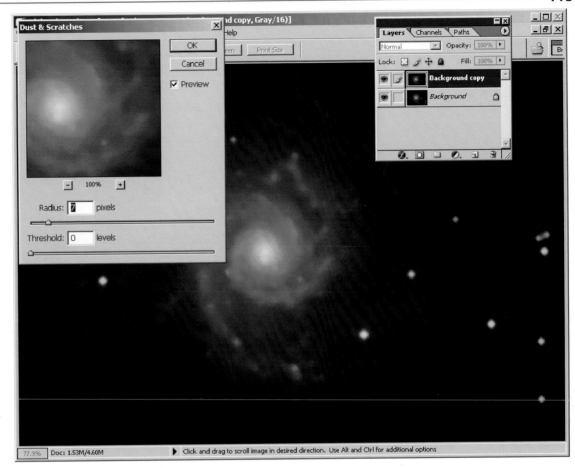

Generally speaking, you should use the smallest practical radius setting when you are removing stars. The potential problems are severe enough that it pays to look closely at the results of various radius settings. In the most extreme cases, you can select the largest stars by hand. Very large and bright stars often require special processing anyway, and leaving them out of the selection at this stage is not necessarily a problem. It might, in fact, enable you to give such stars the special attention they require.

This image of M74 contains some fairly large and bright stars, so a large radius is required to tame those bright stars. The figure at right shows the result with a radius of 13 pixels.

The changes to the galaxy itself are fairly extreme at this large radius. Keep in mind that the galaxy portion of this layer will not be used in the final image. This is a temporary layer. What we are concerned about here is getting rid of the stars without making excessive changes to the galaxy. As noted earlier, you do want to avoid making such extreme changes to the galaxy that it will be picked up by the Difference blend mode we are about to apply.

The natural question to ask at this point is "How do you tell when the large, bright stars are dark enough?" While there is no hard and fast rule for this, the general answer can be found in what happens at the next step (selecting the stars). As long as the stars are reasonably darker, you'll be able to select them with the Color Range dialog (*Select» Color Range...* menu item). If you find that you can't properly select the brightest stars, it is likely that you didn't use a large enough radius. You can use Photoshop®'s History palette to undo one or more steps, and try again. Or you can use the *Elliptical Marquee* tool to add the largest stars manually after use of Color Range.

Set Blend Mode

Here comes the neat part. Make sure that the ***Background copy*** layer is selected in the Layers palette. Click on the blend mode drop-down list in the Layers palette (see figure at right for the location of this list). Choose the *Difference* blend mode.

The blend mode determines how the top layer blends with layers below it. In the case of the Difference blend mode, only pixels that are different between the two layers are going to be visible.

What's different between the two layers? The most obvious difference is the top image doesn't have much in the way of stars. This means that the stars will show up when

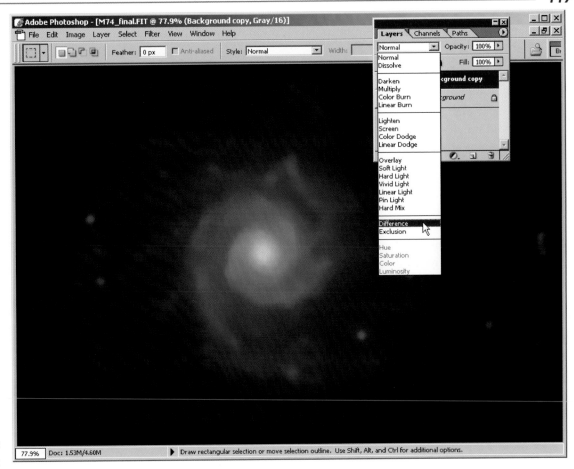

the Difference blend mode is applied. You can see the result of applying the Difference blend mode on the following page.

The Dust & Scratches filter also made some changes to the galaxy, so parts of the galaxy are also going to show up with this blend mode. You can either go back and use a smaller

radius, or continue and use manual methods to remove any galaxy portions from the selection. As you become more skilled in the use of this technique, you'll be able to judge the radius setting to minimize the amount of manual corrections you need to make.

The image at right shows approximately what you should see if you are following along with this tutorial. The exact number, brightness, and size of stars that show up depends on the radius you used in the Dust & Scratches filter.

❧ TIP: You can select different sizes of stars to perform different operations. For example, suppose that you want to isolate the dim stars. You can use a smaller radius, which will leave the brightest stars intact. The Difference blend mode will contain only the stars that changed.

Why would you want to select just some of the stars? Consider this complicated but useful operation:

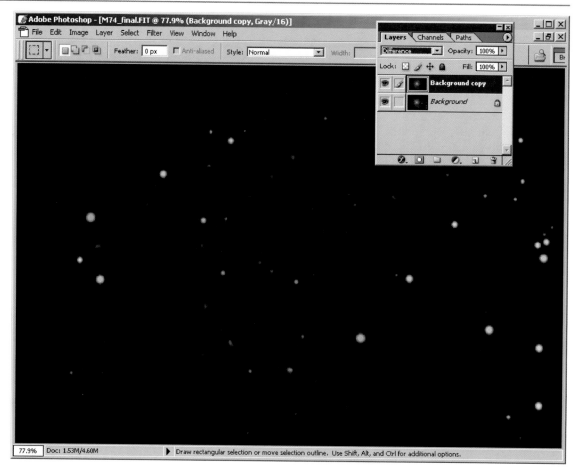

1 Use a small radius in Dust & Scratches

2 Set Blend mode to Difference

3 Select the dim stars with Color Range, and save selection

4 Use History palette to undo Dust & Scratches

5 Redo Dust & Scratches with large enough radius to select all stars

6 Set blend mode to Difference

7 Select all stars, and then subtract the saved selection, leaving just the bright stars

Select Stars

To access the Color Range dialog, use the Select » Color Range... menu item

The Color Range tool allows you to select pixels based on their color and brightness. Since this image is black and white, selection will be based on brightness alone.

❧ TIP: When you need to select by brightness in a color-only (RGB) image, duplicate the layer, desaturate the copy, and then use the copy to create the selection. Delete the copy, and then use the selection.

Click on a star with the eyedropper cursor to start the selection. The figure at right shows a few bright stars selected. The red color shows unselected areas, but only if you set *Quick Mask* as the preview.

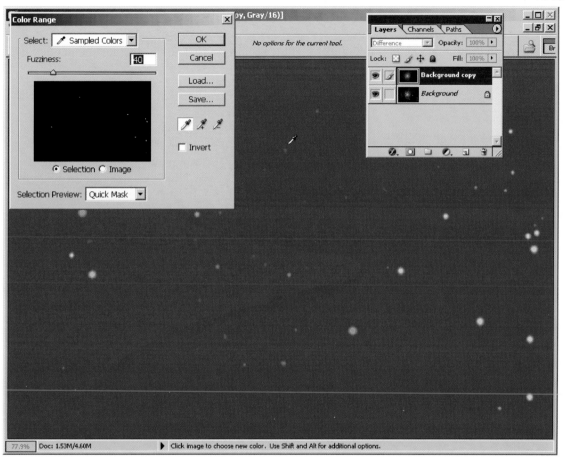

Pixels with a similar brightness level will be selected throughout the image. Typically, there will be dimmer or brighter stars that remain unselected. To select additional pixels

without losing the ones you have already selected, click on the middle eyedropper (it has a small plus sign next to it). Now use this eyedropper to add to the initial selection. Continue until you have as many stars selected as you need. Look carefully for star cores that go unselected, and click on them.

The figure at right shows a selection that goes about as far as possible, selecting both bright and dim stars.

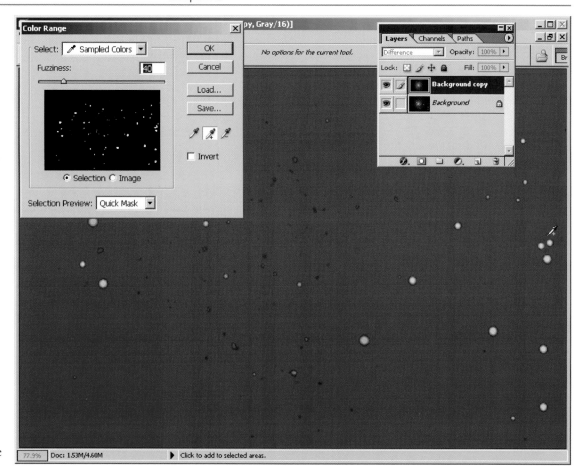

The galaxy is also very bright, and because sections of the galaxy are revealed by the Difference blend mode, we have a mixture of stars and galaxy parts in the selection. You'll learn how to remove the galaxy portions of the selection shortly.

How do you know when to stop selecting with the plus eyedropper? This is a judgement call. If you only want to shrink the largest stars, don't include the dim stars. If you have the patience to manually remove galaxy chunks from the selection, go ahead and select even the very dimmest stars.

Click the *OK* button to create the selection.

❧ Tɪᴘ: Because there were some really large stars in this image, we did not enlarge the radius far enough in the Dust & Scratches tool to completely get rid of them. This means that, in the blended image, the core of the largest stars will be dimmer than the edges. When selecting, pay special attention to the brighter stars. If the cores of the large stars are reddish (that is, unselected), make sure to click on these cores to include the central portion of the stars in the selection. If you forget, use the Elliptical Marque with the Shift key afterwards to select the unselected cores.

The result of the selection is shown at right. It doesn't look like much because the temporary layer is still visible. Now that we have created the selection based on differences, you can hide or delete the temporary layer. To hide the layer, click on the eyeball in the *Background copy* layer to toggle visibility off. This reveals the Background layer, with the selection still visible (below). Or right click and choose *Delete Layer*.

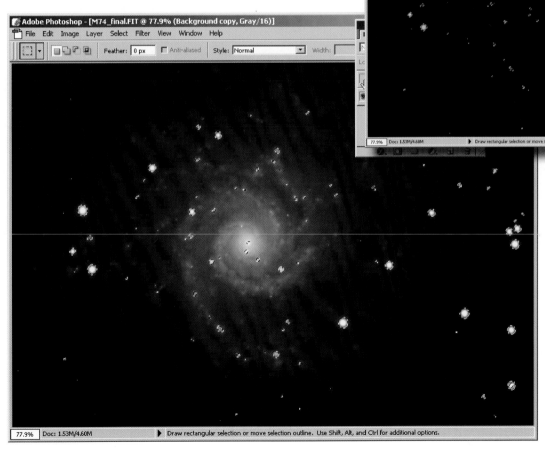

As you can see, the stars are selected but so are the some of the brightest portions of the galaxy.

Not all images will leave you with this type of manual cleanup. And, as pointed out earlier, you can choose a smaller radius to minimize this problem (at the cost of having to select the brighter stars manually).

Clean Up the Selection

To manually remove the galaxy portions from the selection, go to the tools palette and click on the *Rectangular Marquee* tool (see figure at left). If this is not the default tool, click and hold on whatever marquee tool is active. A fly-out menu will appear, and you can select the Rectangular Marquee from the fly-out list.

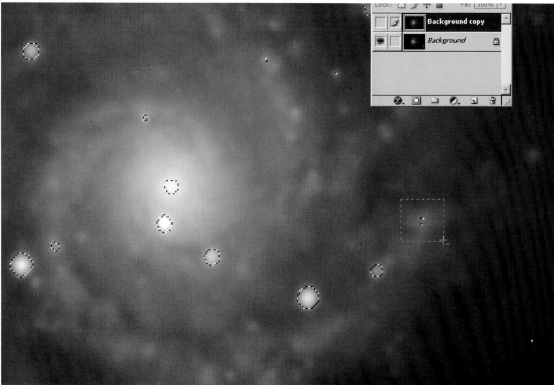

❧ Tip: You can use the Shift and Alt keys when making selections to add to or remove from the selection. The Shift key adds; the Alt key removes.

In this example, we want to remove portions of the selection that belong to the galaxy. Hold down the Alt key while dragging out rectangles with the Rectangular Marquee tool, as shown above. When you release the mouse button, the portion of the selection surrounded by the rectangle will go away.

Continue in this fashion until the galaxy portions are removed from the selection.

❧ Tip: You will find that enlarging the image to at least 100%, and perhaps even 200%, will make your job easier. You can use scroll bars to work your way around the image if the image is too large to see in its entirety when enlarged. You can also hold down the space bar and drag the image.

❧ Tip: Some of the galaxy features are round, just like stars. But the stars are typically brighter than most galaxy features.

When you are done with cleanup, all that remains selected are the stars. You might want to save the selection at this point, so that if you make a mistake later on you can reload the selection.

To save a selection, use the Select » Save Selection menu item

What can you do with your collection of stars? You could apply a filter to them, such as the minimum filter, to tighten up the stars for a more aesthetic appearance. Another useful technique is to apply an unsharp mask to the stars using a non-zero threshold setting to avoid sharpening any diffraction effects too much.

Tip: You can also subtract the stars selection from other selections to avoid applying filters to the stars. For example, you could select the galaxy with the color range tool, and then subtract the stars in front of the galaxy before sharpening the selection. You could then sharpen the stars in front of the galaxy using different settings.

But before you try applying filters to the selected stars, there are some things you can do to modify the selection to avoid creating image artifacts as a result of your actions. If you are going to be subtracting the stars selection from other selections, you might use different modifications, but the idea is the same.

Expand and Feather the Selection

If you were to apply a filter to the stars with the existing selection, there would be a harsh edge around the star. Expanding and feathering the selection creates a soft selection zone around the star, and any filtering that you do will be feathered between the star and the surrounding image.

To expand a selection, use the Select » Modify » Expand menu item

If the stars are bloated or have a soft extended edge, then expand by a larger number of pixels. If the stars are already small and tight, expand by a smaller number of pixels. In this example, star bloat is considerable, so a value of 5 or 6 would be appropriate. In general, expansion values from 3 to 7 pixels will handle most situations. I chose a value of 5 in this case, but there isn't a single right answer.

❧ Tip: The expansion applies to the entire selection. Bloated stars might demand a large expansion, but the smaller stars might wind up with too much area around them for good processing. You'll need to strike a balance. The expansion creates a small buffer zone around each star, as shown above.

The buffer zone helps, but it's not going to solve all of the potential problems. Feathering will soften the effect of any filters that we apply.

To feather the edge of a selection, use the Select » Feather menu item

The amount of feathering depends on the amount of expansion. In general, you want the feathering to be about 50–75% of the expansion. Since we expanded by 5 pixels, a feather of 3 pixels is about right. You won't see much change in the appearance of the selection, but the edge of the selection is feathered nonetheless.

Feathering changes the amount by which an effect is applied to the pixels in the selection. Without feathering, all pixels in a selection get 100% of the effect. The figure below shows a normal selection at left, and a 5-pixel feather at right. Note that feathering extends inside and outside of the selection.

The figure below was created by saving the selections into an alpha channel. The brightness of each pixel in the channel determines how much of the filter is applied within the selection. White pixels get 100% of the filter, and black pixels get none. Gray shades get an appropriate percentage of the filter applied to that pixel. For example, a pixel that is 43% gray will get 57% of the filter effect.

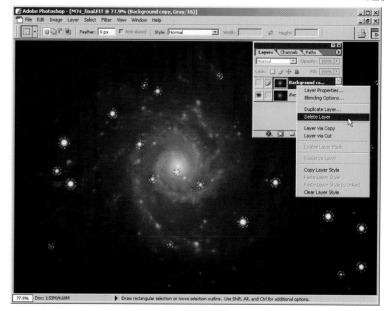

There is no further need for the ***Background copy*** layer; it was only needed to create the selection of stars. If you wish, you can delete the Background copy layer. Right click on the name of the layer you want to delete, and choose Delete Layer from the pop-up menu (see above).

❧ Tip: If you are satisfied with the expanded and feathered selection, you can also save this selection. You can save any number of selections for re-use at a later time. Be sure to give saved selections a descriptive name so that you know what it is later. For example, I would use a name like "Stars only, feathered" for a selection like this one.

Selection to Layer

You could just start operating on the stars using the selection. But you might want to do more than one operation. Or you might want to use blend modes with your stars (for example, to make round stars out of elongated ones as shown in chapter 8). To do such things, you'll need to turn the selection into a layer. You can copy the selection to the clipboard and paste it, which will create a new layer.

Another method is to right click in the image, and choose *Layer via Copy* from the context menu as shown in the figure at right. This creates a new layer (default name: Layer 1), as shown in the Layers palette.

You can also use the *Layer » New » Layer via Copy* menu item to turn the selection into a layer.

❧ Tip: To rename the layer, right click the layer name in the Layers palette, and choose *Layer Properties...* from the pop-up menu. Enter an appropriate name, such as "Stars modified."

To see the new layer's contents, you can hide the Background layer. Click on the *eyeball icon* on the left of the Background layer item in the Layers palette. With the Background layer hidden, the stars layer shows up clearly as shown at right.

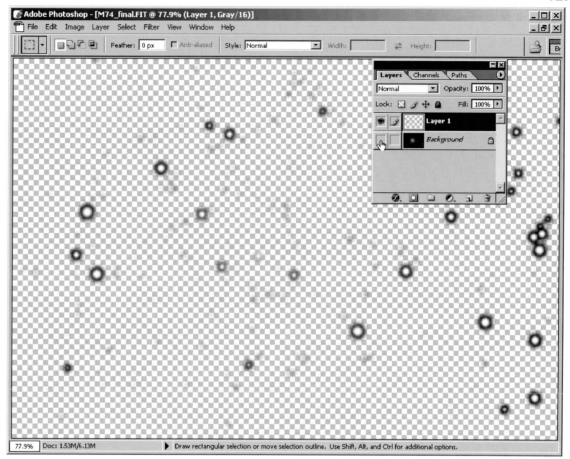

The stars are surrounded by a nicely feathered buffer zone of background. This insures that whatever filter you apply will not have a hard edge. This type of blending is always desirable. Except as noted elsewhere, I use a larger feather for sharpening and a smaller feather radius for smoothing.

NOTE: Some bits of galaxy and background remain selected, as shown by the faint gray "dirt" in the selection. You can clean this up with the Eraser tool.

The light gray color of these background areas tells you that they are not strongly selected (they are heavily feathered), and so you might not notice anything in these areas when you apply a filter to the layer. On the other hand, if you have good data, you don't want to risk some unexpected filter effects! Erasing the faint gray traces will prevent problems.

As always, use your judgment about whether to clean these up in any given image. I've left the gray traces alone here.

Filter Examples

Once you have selected the stars in an image, you can apply some filters to change the appearance of the stars. If you hid the Background layer to see only the stars layer, reveal it now by clicking in the same area where the eyeball was.

To display the Minimum filter's dialog, use the Filter»Other»Minimum menu item

With very few exceptions, you will use a Radius setting of 1 pixel for tightening up bloated stars. Even a value of 1 will sometimes be too much, requiring the use of the *Edit»Fade* menu item.

2ᚷ TIP: You can use the Fade tool to modify nearly any effect in the Photoshop® toolbox. However, you just use Fade immediately after applying a filter. Make sure the Preview checkbox is checked, and then observe the result with different Opacity settings.

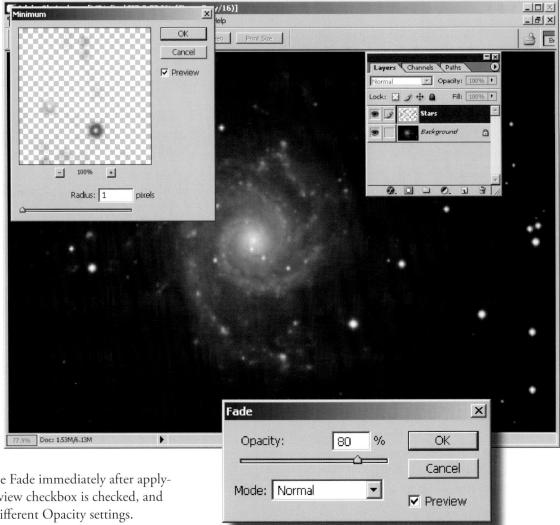

Another useful filter for tightening up stars is the Unsharp Mask.

To display the Unsharp Mask dialog, use the Filter » Sharpen » Unsharp Mask menu item

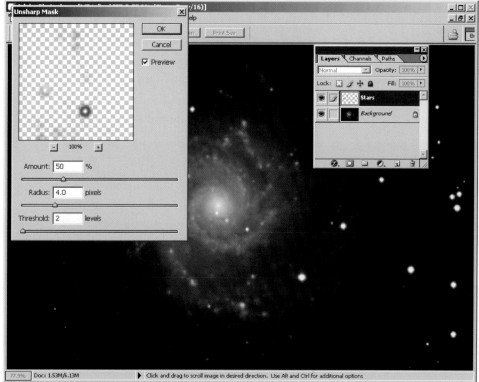

❧ TIP: Before using a filter, make sure that you have selected the appropriate layer in the Layers palette. If you aren't seeing the result you are looking for, it is often because you are simply operating on the wrong layer!

When you are using this tool to tighten up fat stars, you generally want to use a non-zero threshold setting. This will avoid creating excessive artifacts around the stars, and allow you a higher degree of overall sharpening than you could get by conventional means.

In this example the settings are fairly typical for star bloat reduction: a radius of 4 pixels, and a threshold of 2 pixels. A larger radius would tighten up the stars further, but often at the cost of ruining the roundness of the stars. A smaller radius will be more subtle if required.

❧ TIP: I almost always leave the Amount set at 50%. This means that the sharpened image will be combined approximately half and half with the original image. This greatly reduces the occurrence of artifacts from sharpening. Most of the time, even the bright areas of your images have enough noise

in them to result in sharpening artifacts if you use an Amount greater than 50%.

Once you are done processing the stars layer, combine it with the Background layer before you do any other processing. Otherwise, the histograms of the two layers will diverge, creating an ugly boundary between them.

❧ TIP: If you do need to operate on just the non-star portions of the image, you can use your saved selection to do so.

Review

Star selection is a bit complicated, but after practicing it a few times you'll get the hang of it. I suggest trying out star selection on a variety of images so that you get a feel for how it works with different sizes and types of stars and images.

Key points to ponder:

- Star selection depends on a number of Photoshop® tools. As you learn more about how the tools work, you'll discover clever ways to modify the basic methods described in this exercise. For example, as you learn more about selections, you can develop better techniques for cleaning up non-star portions of the Color Range selection.

- The Dust & Scratches tool is the foundation of this process. If you don't like where the process is going in later stages, perhaps you need to go back and re-do the Dust & Scratches filter, using a larger or smaller radius. (The radius determines how aggressively you can select stars.)

- Star selections depends heavily on your knowledge of Photoshop® selections. Many other procedures do, too. The more you know about selection tools, and about how to use saved selections to modify existing selections, the more you can accomplish with Zones. Any standard Photoshop® book (or even the excellent help files) will clue you in to the many ways you can make use of selections—creating them, changing them, and moving them around.

In addition to manipulating the star data as shown in the examples in this chapter, you will no doubt come up with some methods of your own. Stars represent the brightest of the Bright Zone, and having the ability to operate on just this portion of the image creates opportunities for improving the appearance of your

The Crab Nebula

Chapter 6

Controlling Color

Controlling Color

Objective

Achieve a correct color balance between the red, green, and blue channels in an RGB or LRGB image.

Techniques

- Removing color bias (correct setting of black points in individual color channels)
- Balancing color
- Adjusting saturation to a pleasing level
- Understanding and dealing with color noise levels

Tools

- Photoshop® Levels
- Photoshop® Polygonal Lasso Tool
- Photoshop® Color Balance
- Photoshop® Hue/Saturation

Description

Color balancing is often a very trying experience, even if you have been processing images for a long time. For most of us, the eye isn't as accurate at color balancing as we would like it to be. This occurs because the human eye is color-adaptive. That is, we can shift our color perception without realizing it. For example, we have no problem seeing colors "correctly" under varying lighting conditions. Daylight color balance and fluorescent color balance are very different. Daylight is what we are used to, but fluorescent lighting has a very strong green cast. Our eyes remove this green cast for us and allow us to see normally. But this ability isn't very useful when you are trying to remove a green cast from a light-polluted image!

You will learn how to use the Levels dialog to establish correct color. This takes the eyes' adaptability out of the equation, and gives you a standard against which to judge the quality of your color. As you learn more about controlling color, you'll also learn how to recognize more easily when your eyes are playing tricks. This allows you to develop better color processing skills, even without the reference of an image histogram.

Definitions

Black point: Sets the darkest value in the image—all darker values will be rendered black. For proper color balance in the background of an image, the black points in all three color channels should match with respect to the data peaks in the channel histograms.

Channel: Red, Green, and Blue are the color channels. "Channel" is also a technical term in Photoshop®, referring not only to color channels but also to alpha and spot channels. Alpha channels are grayscale images that define a selection. Spot channels are used for printing; they specify where spot colors are to appear in the final printed materials.

Color Balance: The strength of all three color channels is equal and appropriate. When color is out of balance, the image will not have accurate colors. The pseudo white point is used as a guide to accurate color balancing.

Gamma: A tool that adjusts brightness and contrast simultaneously using a midpoint adjustment. Gamma adjustments lighten or darken an image. A Gamma adjustment greater than 1.0 will add more of that color; a Gamma adjustment of less than 1.0 will reduce the contribution of that color. For color balancing, apply gamma adjustments to individual color channels.

Gradient: Usually the result of light pollution, a gradient is an uneven brightening of the image. The image is bright on one area, with the brightness fading away across the image. The brighter side of the gradient is closer to the source of the light pollution, such as a city light dome or a streetlight.

Histogram: A graph that shows the relative number of pixels at each brightness value. The greater the number of pixels at a given brightness level, the higher the peak. Each color channel has its own histogram which you can alter using Levels, Curves, and other tools. Levels adjustments are common; Curves adjustments to a single color channel are risky because it becomes much harder to control color. You can also view and modify the combined RGB histogram when appropriate.

Levels: A Photoshop® tool for making linear adjustments to the image's histogram.

Linear: Brightness and Contrast adjustments that preserve the internal brightness relationships of the image.

LRGB: A color image composed of a luminance (black and white) layer plus the three basic color channels (red, green, and blue).

Midpoint: Levels adjustment used to adjust image Gamma.

Non-Linear: Brightness and Contrast adjustments that alter the internal brightness relationships of the image.

RGB: A color image composed of the three basic color channels: Red, Green, and Blue.

Selection: An area of the image to which processing or filters will be applied. When a selection is active, only the area of the image within the selection can be affected by your actions. Photoshop® contains numerous and powerful tools for creating and modifying selections. Selections can also be saved and restored later. You use selections to operate on a specific zone in the image.

Photoshop® Tips

The Levels and Curves dialogs are the mainstays of Photoshop® image processing. They are as useful for working with color as they are for luminance-only images.

Levels for Color Channels

The Levels dialog displays a histogram of the image. There are three sliders below the histogram that allow you to set the image's black point, midpoint (gamma), and white point.

When you are processing a color layer, you can apply Levels changes to either the entire layer, or to a single color channel. The Levels dialog's Channel drop-down list, shown at right, allows you to choose whether to operate on a single channel or the entire layer. You can also use the keyboard shortcuts shown in the drop-down list to quickly change channels.

❧ Tip: You can also control which channel you are operating on using the Channels palette. However, picking a channel in the Levels dialog is faster and more flexible for the types of processing you'll be doing in this exercise.

Why would you want to make Levels changes to a single channel? Well, there are good reasons and there are risks, too. The primary risk when making Levels changes to a single channel is that you can easily make a mess of the color balance. If you follow the guidelines in this chapter, however, you can avoid those risks.

❧ Tip: You can improve your success in adjusting individual channels with levels by making sure that the Histo-

gram palette is displayed before you open the Levels dialog. This allows you to preview the changes you are making while observing the effects on all three color histograms together.

The primary reason for making Levels changes to individual channels is to correct color bias. When you are making color exposures, you are using an estimate of color exposure times based on the equipment you are using and the current atmospheric conditions. If there is light pollution present, that will often have a profound (and very negative) effect on color balance. High clouds can scatter blue light, as can imaging at a low elevation. Even if your exposures compensate for these things, your color bias/balance can still be incorrect.

Using the techniques in this exercise, you can correct the color in your images.

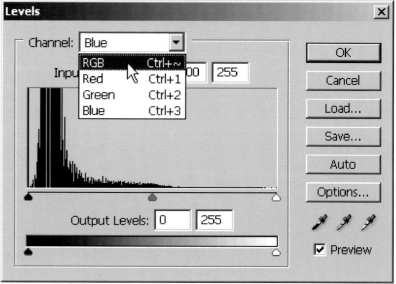

True Color?

We often take color for granted. Most of us make a very simple assumption: the color we see is the true color of what is around us. Unfortunately, color is a very arbitrary and uncertain commodity. The color you see might not be the color that another person sees. Some folks are color blind. Some folks have a greater range of colors, some have less.

The concept of "true color" is problematic right from the start. When you consider that monitors, printers, and the human eye all treat color differently, the problem gets complicated in a hurry. Ultimately, color is in the eye of the beholder.

But wait—there's more! There are literally millions of colors out there. But our eyes synthesize colors using just three filters (red, green, and blue). Sampling such a broad range of data points with just three filters means that even a tiny difference in one filter—whether it is our eyes, our monitor, our printers, or the glass filters used for color CCD images—complicates the task of capturing color accurately.

What a mess! What we need is some good news about working with color. Despite the potential pitfalls, you can get very good color by concentrating on four areas:

- Color bias
- Color balance
- Color noise
- Color intensity (saturation)

Color Bias

A color bias exists when one or more colors flood the background of an image. The root cause of color bias is unequal black point settings in the affected color channel.

The image below shows an example of color bias. This is a two-color bias: mostly a green bias, but some blue bias as well. You might imagine that this results from having too much green, and that's sort of correct. The issue isn't just how much green (or blue) there is; the issue is the way in which there is too much of a color.

The cause of color bias is a color offset. This means that there is too much color in the sense of a container with a false bottom, as illustrated below. The amount of green is correct; it's just that every point is a little too bright.

With color bias, the extra brightness is the same at every point. If one pixel is too bright in green by 10 units, then every other pixel is too bright by 10 units.

The separate red, green, and blue histograms shown at right demonstrate a color bias. Notice that the histograms are offset. The further to the right the histogram peak is offset, the greater the bias in that color. The histograms at right are for the M51 image on the previous page, and they confirm the diagnosis: a small blue bias, and a larger green bias.

The fix is simple: subtract the extra green from every pixel by adjusting the black point for each channel.

The red channel has the least bias, so the first step is to raise the black point of the red channel using Levels in Photo-shop®. You raise it the same way you would for a luminance image: just to the left of the peak. Then repeat for green and blue.

If you do this correctly, the background of the image will take on a neutral (or nearly neutral) gray, as shown in the example on the opposite page.

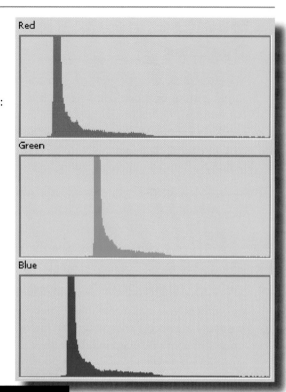

A color bias is like a false bottom in a container. In this example, there is too much green. Removing the false bottom (by adjusting the green black point using Levels) will remove the bias.

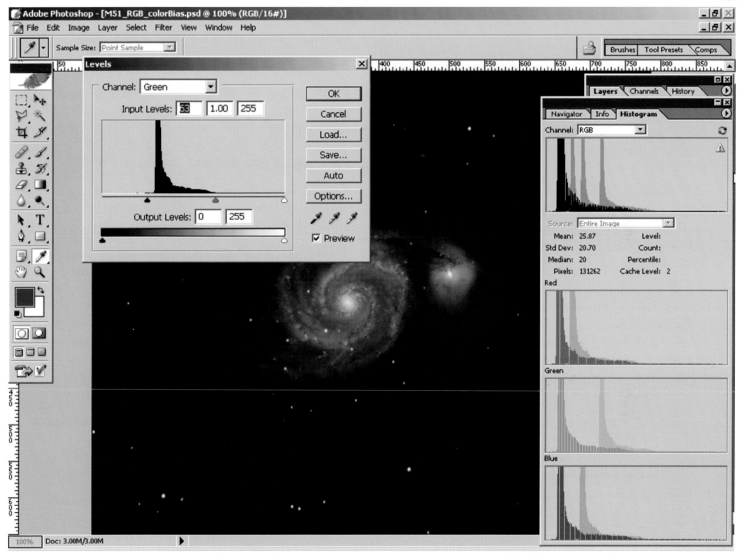

Use the Histogram palette to evaluate Levels changes for color channels.

Color Balance

Color balance means that the strength of the color channels is the same. If one or more colors is stronger or weaker than the others, you will see a color imbalance.

Color bias is characterized by an off-color background. In the case of color balance problems, the off-color will be in the objects themselves.

Very important: *Always* (yep, every time; this cannot be over-emphasized!) correct color bias before you correct color balance. If you try to correct color balance before color bias, you will make a Grand Mess of Things, and will have to start over. Make it a habit to correct color bias before you do anything else with your color images.

Color balance is like a container that is too full. The figure below shows how color imbalance can be visualized. Unlike a color bias, which can simply be subtracted, a color imbal-ance requires more subtle forms of correction. The problem is a proportional one: if pixel A is too bright by 10 units, pixel B might be too bright by 20 units. The good news is that brighter pixels will have proportionally more color. Photoshop® comes to the rescue with tools that understand this relationship and make it easy to correct color imbalance.

Sources of Color Balance Problems

Color balance problems come from various sources. The most common are incorrect exposure times, incorrect number of color exposures, and processing mistakes.

The exposure times for red, green, and blue filters are often different. For example, with my STL-11000 camera, I use 15-minute red exposures, 9-minute green exposures, and 18-minute blue exposures. These exposure times account for the different amounts of light that pass through each filter, the quantum efficiency of the CCD sensor at various wavelengths, and so on.

In many cases, the camera/filter manufacturer will supply suggested exposure ratios. You can also use software, such as Don Goldman's RGB Weight Calculator:

http://www.astrodon.com/

to determine starting exposure ratios.

You can also gather data and perform calculations to generate exposure ratios yourself. A method based on the solar analog method can be found at:

http://www.ghg.net/akelly/artdraf7.htm

Recognizing Color Balance Problems

If the background of the image is neutral, that means that there are no color bias issues with the image/layer. You cannot solve a color problem unless you deal with color bias first.

You can also use your knowledge of the structure of astronomical objects to diagnose color problems. For example, HII regions (strong H-alpha emissions) are red. In some cases, a bright star emitting lots of UV radiation might create some blue illumination as well (this is dust reflecting blue light, not an emission).

Other examples:

• Spiral galaxy cores are often red

• Star birth regions where the gasses of formation have been blown away are typically blue because of many young, hot stars

• Reflection nebulosity is typically blue

Evaluating Color Balance

For terrestrial photography, a "white balance" is used to correct color balance. But this is not simple to do with an astronomical image.

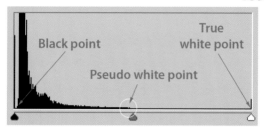

Instead of using the image's true white point, you can use what I call the pseudo white point. The image at right shows the black point (used to remove color bias), the true white point (brightest, often saturated, stars) and the pseudo white point (brightness of non-star details in the image).

The saturated stars in an image make conventional white balance difficult to impossible. However, the pseudo white point is a useful tool for measuring color balance—as long as you temper your measurements with some knowledge of the actual color of objects and the things that make them up.

The pseudo white point on the histogram works for color balance because of what it represents—unsaturated color levels in each channel. As noted above, simply lining up the pseudo white points won't give you balanced color. But observing the differences in location of the pseudo white points in the three color channels will give you important information about where and why you have a color balance problem.

The most useful way to view the color channel histograms is with the histogram palette. To display this palette, use the *Window » Histogram* menu item. Use the palette menu to turn on *All Channels View* and *Show Channels in Color*.

❧ Tɪᴘ: Showing all color channels at one time makes the histogram palette large. You can minimize it by double-clicking on the palette's caption bar. This works for any palette.

Fixing Color Balance Problems

The figure at bottom right shows part of an image that is very badly out of color balance, as well as the all-channels view of the histogram palette.

As you can see from the histograms, there is no color bias present in this example—that has already been cleaned up. What remains is a rather horrid green color problem. While this example is simulated, I have had many occasions to image from light-polluted locations (such as my Seattle-area yard) where the light pollution was this bad or worse.

The histograms show the story. I have added arrows to indicate the approximate location of the pseudo white point for each channel. The green channel histogram shows why the image is so green—the pseudo white point stretches out much further than it does in the red and blue channels.

Notice that, even allowing for the length difference, the histograms have different shapes. There is a bump on the red histogram just to the left of the arrow. The blue histogram has a noticeable straight segment sloping at 45 degrees, just to the right of the main peak.

These are reminders that the goal isn't to line up the pseudo white points exactly, but to use it as a guide to know in what direction to proceed with processing.

While it is possible to use Levels and/or Curves to correct color problems, by far the easiest method for attacking this problem is the Color Balance tool. Even the name gives away how useful this tool is for the problem at hand!

The figure on the next page shows the Color Balance tool in action. The green imbalance is exaggerated. The Color Balance tool consists of three sliders. Each slider affects a specific color channel relative to the other two.

For example, the Cyan/Red slider adds more red by moving to the right, or increases cyan by moving to the left. Since cyan is a mixture of green and blue, reducing red has the visual effect of making the green and blue channels stronger.

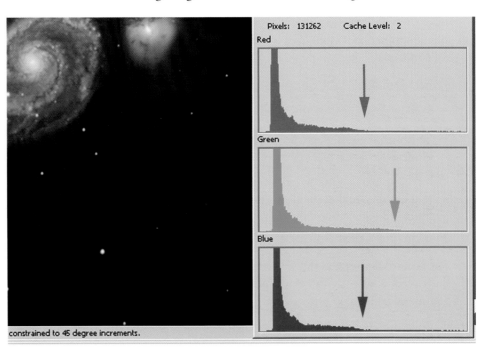

constrained to 45 degree increments.

In this example, there is too much green, so the slider has been moved toward Magenta. Note how the image has taken on a magenta hue.

After making the obvious adjustment for less green, it was apparent that there was a bit of a deficiency in red, so that slider has been moved a little to the right.

The numbers that correspond to the slider adjustments allow for fine tuning. For example, we need a bit less magenta, so we could manually edit −72 to −60 and review.

Note that the Histogram palette shows both the existing histogram (light) and a preview of the new histogram (dark). The pseudo white points are much closer to lining up.

🎗 TIP: Notice that the bias level changes with the change in color balance. You will always need to visit Levels after you balance color to remove this bias.

The Tone Balance section of the Color Balance tool allows you to adjust color balance for the Dim,

Middle, and Bright zones (Shadows, Midtones, Highlights). For most images, adjusting the Midtones will be best. Occasionally, you will need to adjust highlights separately, as in the M51 example. Shadow color balance seldom comes into play because that is most likely a color bias issue, not a color balance problem. If there is a severe color balance problem, you can sometimes get better results by using different settings for Shadows, Midtones, and Highlights.

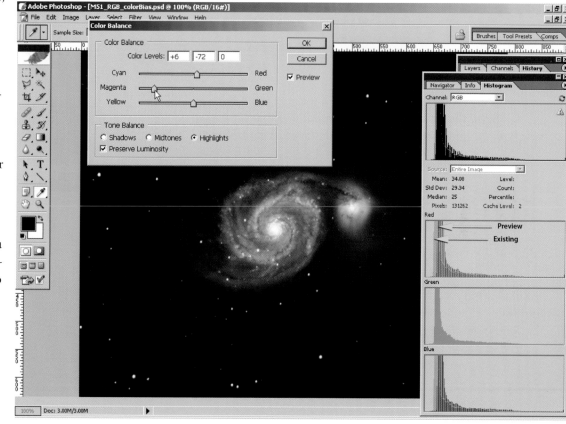

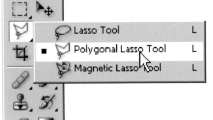

Polygonal Lasso Tool

Photoshop® selections are very powerful. When you use a filter or a tool, only the area within the selection is operated on.

There are many ways to make selections in Photoshop®. One of the most useful is the Lasso tool. The variation called the Polygonal Lasso tool is one of the most useful for astronomical image processing.

🔖 Tip: If the variation of a tool you want isn't the active one, click and hold on the tool. A fly-out menu will appear with the other variations of the tool.

The standard Lasso tool works like a drawing tool—you draw out an area in the image while holding down the left mouse button. When you lift the button, the area bounded by the line you have drawn becomes a Photoshop® selection.

The Lasso tool requires an artist's hand to make accurate selections. If you make the slightest error, the selection won't include the area you want it to. The Polygonal Lasso tool simplifies the art of making irregular selections. Instead of drawing out the entire line, you click at a succession of points to enclose the area you want to select.

Using the Polygonal Lasso tool, click around an object to select it. It doesn't matter how irregular the object is; the Polygonal Lasso can handle just about anything you'll run into.

For example, it is often necessary to apply custom color balancing to planetary nebulae. Most filter sets are designed to provide accurate color for stars and galaxies, but not for the unique color signatures of planetary nebulae. By color balancing the entire image first, and then isolating the planetary nebula with the Polygonal Lasso tool, you can provide accurate color balancing for all parts of the image.

In the image at right, the top image is the overly blue "natural" version of M57. The lower version has been color balanced to adjust for the blue bias for the OIII emissions in the color filters.

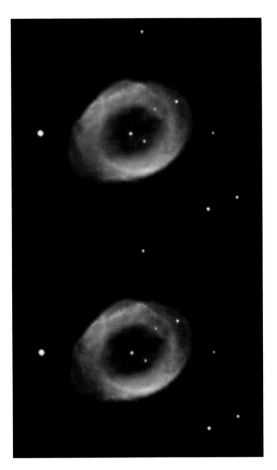

Fixing Color Problems

The source file for this portion of the exercise is a 2x2 binned image of M51, taken with a C14 and an SBIG ST-1001E camera. The color is a little weak because the exposures were not long enough to develop more color.

ᕀ TIP: You can increase color saturation with the *Image»Adjust»Hue/Saturation* tool. Depending on the noise level in the image, a maximum boost of +20 to +50 will be possible.

> *If you would like to follow along with this exercise, open the following file from the DVD in Photoshop® CS (or later):*
>
> **\C6\M51_RGB_curves.psd**

NOTE: For this exercise, you are using a file that has already been processed using the Levels and Curves dialog as described in chapter 2. If you would like to practice using Levels and Curves on the image yourself, open the following file instead:

\C6\M51_RGB.tif

The color balance will be slightly different if you open the TIFF version of the file.

If you open the Levels dialog, you will see a combined histogram that looks pretty normal. The black point could

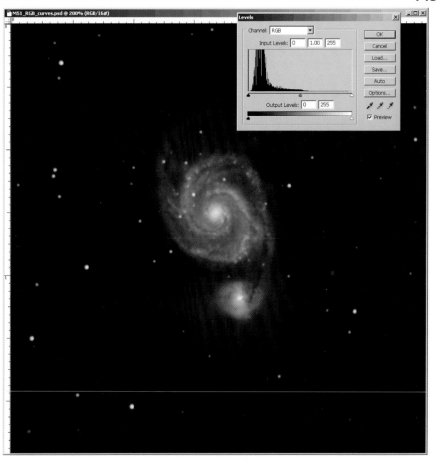

be raised a small amount, nearer to the left side of the main data peak, but otherwise this is a perfectly normal-looking initial histogram, with a peak on the left side and not much of anything as the histogram fades away to the right. Looks, however, can be deceiving, as we'll discover as we pick the histogram apart.

Remove Color Bias

Image»Adjustments»Levels

The Levels dialog displays the image's histogram, a graph of the brightness values in an image. The left side of the histogram maps darker values, and the right side maps brighter values. There are three histograms at right, one showing the brightness values in each of the color channels (red, green, and blue). I used the channel drop-down to display each channel's histogram in turn.

The ideal position for the black point is just to the left of the big, broad peak. I have added red, green, and blue lines to show where the black point should go for each color channel. These are not the same, indicating the presence of a color bias. You cannot properly adjust the black point for this color image by adjusting all three color channels at the same time. Each channel must be adjusted individually.

The misalignment of the histograms creates a color bias, visible in the background. The too-low black points of the red and green channels make those channels brighter. Red and Green combined yield Yellow, so the image has a slightly yellow cast (see figure on previous page).

Adjusting the black points individually will balance the background correctly. To adjust the black points, move the leftmost sliders toward the right for each channel, to a point just left of the peak for that channel. Always keep an eye on the image to make sure you are doing the right thing. Complete these color bias adjustments before moving on.

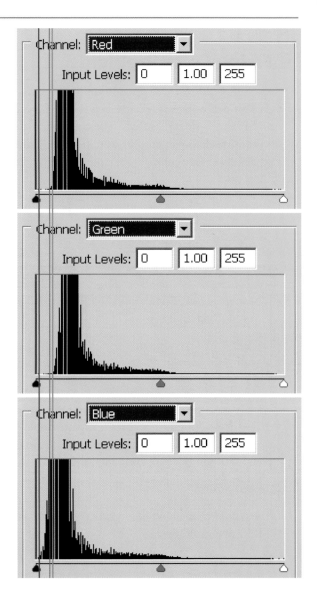

Color Balance

Window » Layers

The image of M51 at right has an overall magenta cast. This means that there is either too much red and blue or not enough green. The colors are out of balance with each other. (Color bias has already been corrected in this image.)

> *If you would like to follow along with this exercise, open the following file from the DVD in Photoshop® CS (or later):*
>
> \C6\M51_LRGB.psd

Interestingly, the image doesn't look horrible despite the color problems. The eye is good at adapting to color problems.

☞ TIP: Make sure you select the color layer as the active layer, as shown at right.

The M51 combined color histogram is shown below, after bias corrections. It looks like an ordinary histogram. Because there is a large black area in the image, subtleties of the histogram cannot be seen. Even if you use the Channel drop-down list to view the individual histograms for the red, green, and blue channels, you won't see a whole lot of visible difference among them. There are small differences, but we can't see them clearly because the histogram is showing us too much information at one time—the histogram includes both the object (where we want to look for imbalance) and the background (which is now neutral thanks to bias corrections).

What we are really interested in is the area immediately around the galaxy. There is a simple way to get the histogram for just this part of the image: use the Photoshop® selection tools to select just the galaxy. The Polygonal Lasso tool is the

best way to do this. Activate the Polygonal Lasso in the Tools palette before you continue.

Click at the edges of the galaxy to make a selection around it. Double click to close the selection. The figure at far right on the next page shows roughly the area you want to enclose with this selection.

NOTE: This selection is temporary. The galaxy shows the color problem most clearly, but the entire image suffers from the color imbalance. By selecting just the galaxy, we view a more spread-out version of the histogram. Because the dim background pixels are not part of the selection, the differences in color channels are easier to see.

It doesn't matter if your selection is exactly like the one shown. The idea is to create a selection that excludes most of the dim background. Even a rectangular selection around the galaxy would be adequate.

The magenta cast can be fixed by boosting the green channel. The following list summarizes what you want to change if you find a given color too strong:

Dominant Color	Correction to Apply
Green cast	Increase red and blue (magenta)
Red cast	Increase green and blue (cyan)
Blue cast	Increase green and red (yellow)
Magenta cast	Increase green
Cyan cast	Increase red
Yellow cast	Increase blue

Color balance problems come from different causes. Light pollution is a common source of color balance problems. If a color balance problem varies across an image, light pollution gradients are often the cause. The solution to color problems from gradients is to fix the gradients in each color channel first, before you follow the procedures outlined here. If there are residual color problems after removing gradients, then you can use these techniques.

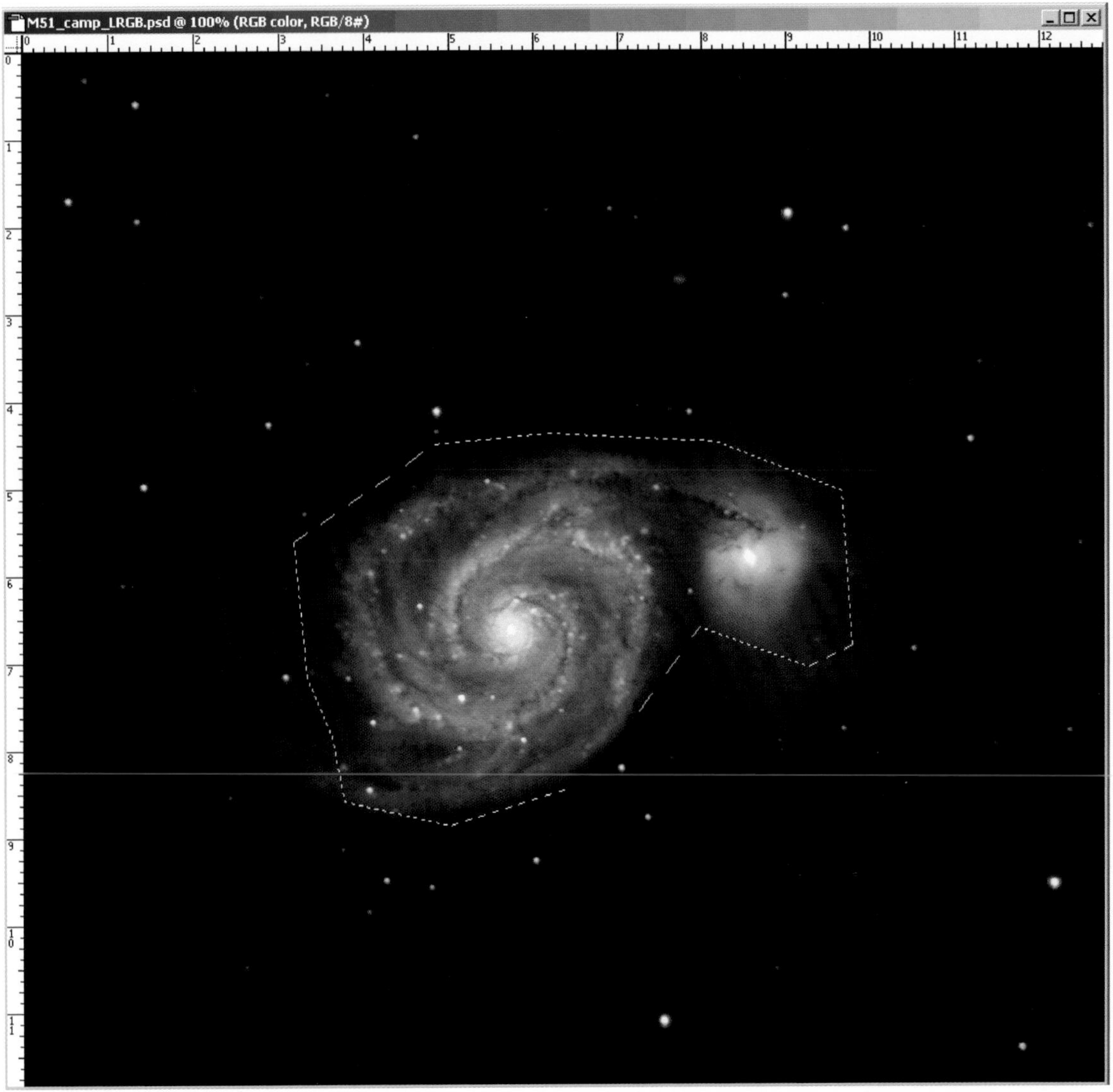

☙ Tip: Russell Croman's Gradient XTerminator is the best method I've found for dealing with all kinds of gradients. See:

http://www.rc-astro.com

Note: You can also create color imbalance while performing other processing steps. Keep an eye on color balance whenever you work on a color layer.

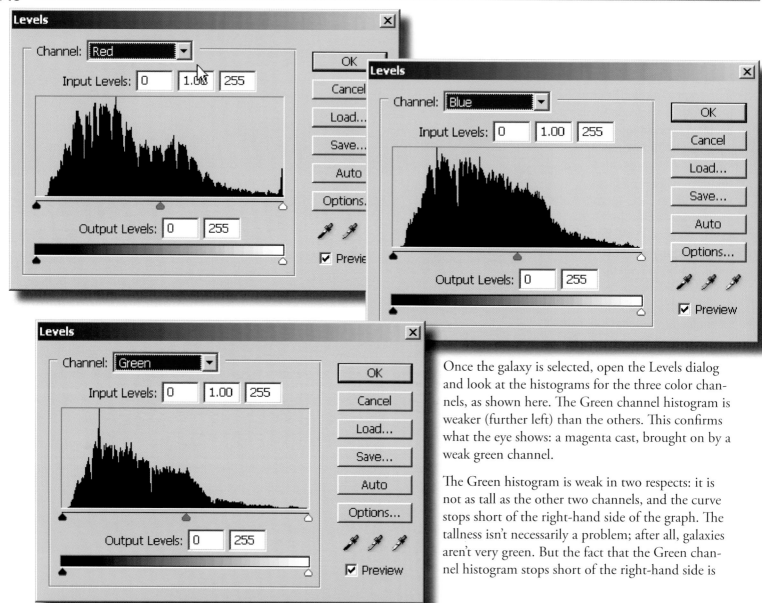

Once the galaxy is selected, open the Levels dialog and look at the histograms for the three color channels, as shown here. The Green channel histogram is weaker (further left) than the others. This confirms what the eye shows: a magenta cast, brought on by a weak green channel.

The Green histogram is weak in two respects: it is not as tall as the other two channels, and the curve stops short of the right-hand side of the graph. The tallness isn't necessarily a problem; after all, galaxies aren't very green. But the fact that the Green channel histogram stops short of the right-hand side is a problem, because it needs to match the Red and Blue channel histograms.

✌ Tip: You can also use the Histogram palette in recent versions of Photoshop® to view and compare the color channel histograms.

You can handle your color corrections with the Levels tool. The most effective method is to move the Midpoint slider (gamma control) to the left to strengthen color in that channel. Watch for noise effects when you do this; you might have to weaken the other channels by moving their Midpoint sliders to the right.

It doesn't usually take much Gamma adjustment to restore color balance. A Gamma setting of 1.09 gets the job done here. Move the middle slider to the left to increase the Gamma. A value above 1.0 brightens a channel.

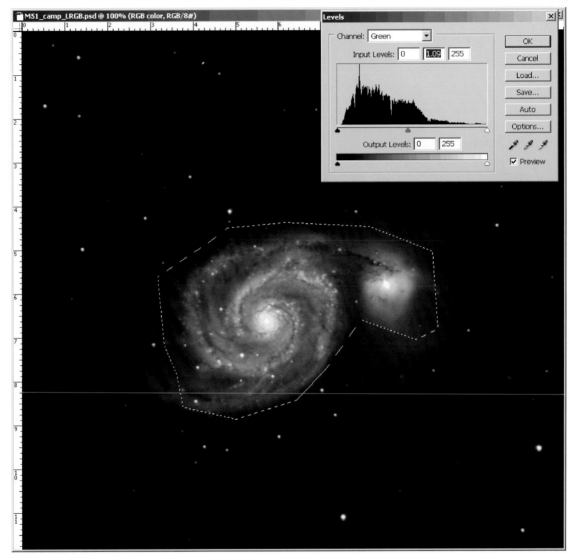

You will seldom find a need for Gamma adjustments that are larger than 1.20, or smaller than 0.80. Exceeding these values will often create excessive saturation or attenuation, and look unnatural.

By selecting just the galaxy, we in effect held a magnifying glass to the histogram. You can now cancel, deselect, and apply the Gamma adjustment to the Green channel of the entire image, as shown at right.

The insert at right shows the resulting histograms for the three color channels. They are now more nearly alike. They will always be somewhat different after balancing because the channels do, after all, contain different information.

NOTE: Any form of color balancing may create a color bias. *Always* check color bias after balancing color.

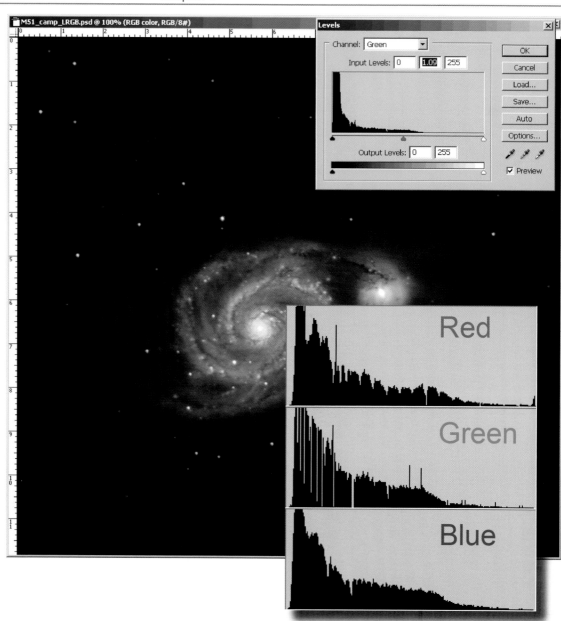

Quick Balance

The preceding example illustrates the long way to do a color balance. I took the long approach because it breaks down color balancing and allows you to see the changes in the image as well as how the changes affect the color channel histograms.

As you get more familiar with the color of objects and the color balancing process, you can use a shortcut: the Color Balance tool.

The image at right shows my estimate of the value to use for the shift away from Magenta and toward Green. Note that the adjustment is 9, and recall that the Gamma adjustment was 1.09. This is not a coincidence; the two adjustments generate similar results.

❧ Tip: Try reducing Red by a small amount. Is the color balance better, or worse?

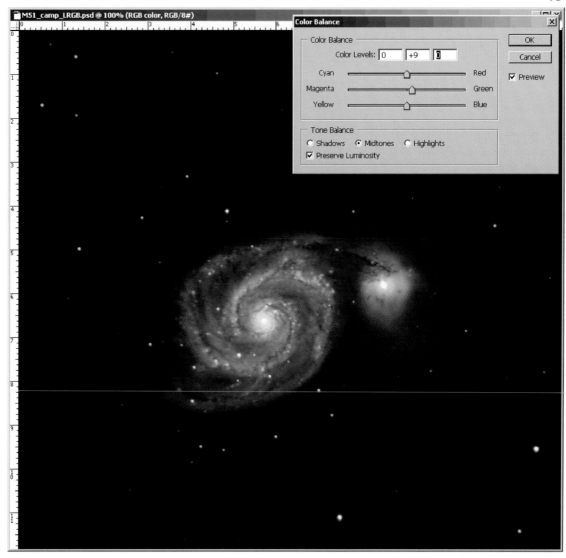

Severe Color Bias

The Cocoon image at right shows a dramatic blue/green color bias. The image histogram at top right shows multiple peaks, a sure sign of severe color bias.

The individual color channel histograms reveal what is happening. The Red histogram peak is at far left. The Green histogram shows a peak near the center of the graph. The Blue channel's histogram is shifted almost as far as the Green channel's.

How did this happen? High clouds moved in as the green and blue images were being taken. This resulted in a much brighter sky background for those two channels.

The cure for this problem is the same one used earlier in this chapter, even though the black points are dramatically offset. Move the black points for each channel to a position just to the left of the main peak. The image on the next page shows how this neutralizes the background. As long as you deal with color bias first, even severe bias is not necessarily fatal.

The bias is severe, so don't expect your first attempt to give you perfect results. Adjust the black points of all three channels, adjusting carefully, after each iteration of Curves (using the Standard Curve).

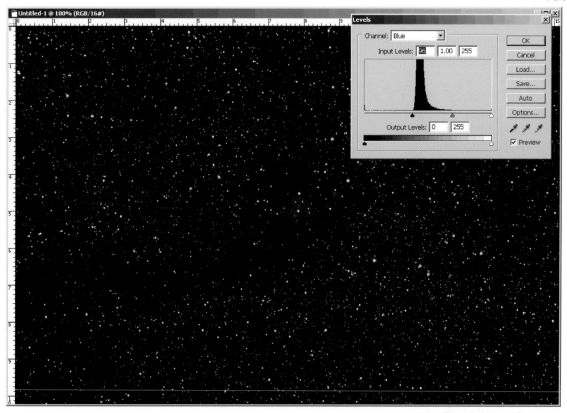

I have included the original color files for this image of the Cocoon online and on the DVD. To try correcting this severe background imbalance yourself, you can either create an RGB image from these files:

\C6\Cocoon_R.fit
\C6\Cocoon_G.fit
\C6\Cocoon_B.fit

or use the already assembled RGB image:

\C6\Cocoon_RGB.psd

If you would like to try an LRGB combine, the luminance image is:

\C6\Cocoon_avg2.fit

Automatic Bias Removal

Photoshop® includes a tool that might prove useful at times. Although you have the highest degree of control when manually tweaking settings, you can get close using automatic bias removal. This feature is called "Auto Color Correction" in Photoshop® CS and later versions.

To display the Auto Color Correction Options dialog, first open the Curves dialog, and then click the *Options...* button. The dialog is shown on the next page.

The automatic correction features are designed for terrestrial photography, but there are some astronomical possibilities. In particular, the "Find Dark & Light color" radio button, despite the naming having nothing to do with histograms, does the job we are looking for.

As you can see in the figure at right, selecting this radio button (red arrow) balances the background, and it makes the color channel histograms line up nicely (histogram palette).

In the earlier example, we set all of the black points optimally (just to the left of the peak). When using this tool, the black points are lined up, but you will still need to finish the job manually using Levels. However, you can operate on the RGB channel instead of having to work with the channels individually (see below).

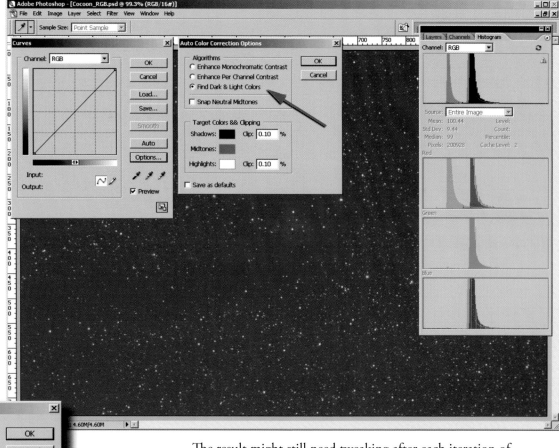

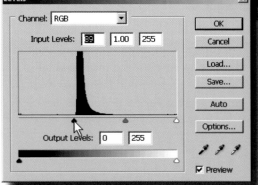

The result might still need tweaking after each iteration of Curves, just as with the manual example earlier. The more you stretch the image with Curves, the more able you are to make subtle corrections.

This Cocoon image isn't a long exposure, so it's still noisy, but despite a horrific color bias, it comes out OK (see right).

Color Balancing Tips

Color balancing has long been seen as a "black art" and for good reason. When you consider the number of places that color balance can go wrong, it seems like a miracle that it ever goes right:

- Changes in the atmosphere can affect color balance. One common cause is high clouds, but dust in the air can also affect color. Both will tend to redden your images because both scatter blue light.

- Elevation above the horizon affects color balance. When you image below about 45 degrees of elevation, you are imaging through more air. Blue is scattered more than red is below this level, so longer blue exposures are required through the blue filter. See the table on the next page to determine how much longer to expose.

- Light pollution can affect color fidelity. Problems occur from the lower signal-to-noise ratio, and from side effects of removing light pollution gradients.

- Failure to get the exact right exposure times in each color can also affect color balance. There are small variations from one batch of filters to the next, so you should take some time to determine the optimal color exposure ratios for your filters. The easy way is with Don Goldman's RGB Weight Calculator, which will get you close. For a more precise calculation, please see this web site:

http://www.ghg.net/akelly/artdraf7.htm

Keys to success:

- Optimal exposure time lowers noise. Color balancing involves stretching the data, and noisy exposures can't be stretched much.

- Always fix color bias first, no matter how minor it is.

- For all but planetary nebulae, use Levels to make an approximate match of the pseudo white points in the color channels. Not all objects have closely matching colors, however. The more you learn about the structures found in nebulae, and the color and emissions of those structures, the better job you will be able to do at color balancing.

Color Noise = Weak Color

The image below is made up of a stack of three RGB images. The image at top right is a single RGB set, which of course means it has more noise. Both images have been smoothed to reduce color noise, but even after smoothing, the images are clearly noisy. Stacking reduces noise, and color smoothing hides noise, but that's not enough to get really good color.

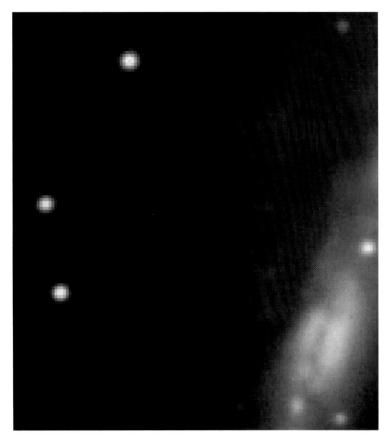

Color smoothing works by reducing the color contrast between adjoining pixels. Programs like MaxIm DL do color smoothing directly, while in Photoshop® you can use a Gaussian Blur on the color layer to achieve a similar result.

The image on facing page at lower left is a blow-up of a small portion of the stacked image before color smoothing. The arrow points to one pixel in particular that illustrates how color

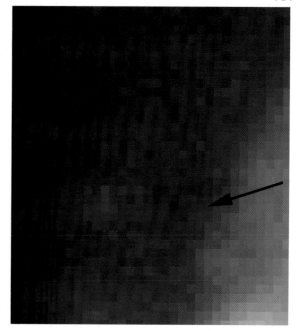

smoothing works. In the image below, that pixel is a very different color than surrounding pixels. Among other things, this indicates that there is a fair amount of color noise present.

The image at right shows what happens after color smoothing. The color contrast between this pixel and the surrounding pixels is reduced. This makes the image look less grainy, but it also reduces the saturation of the colors.

The price you ultimately pay for color smoothing is weaker color. Even if only one color channel is noisy, color smoothing will weaken all of the color channels, not just one.

Color noise affects different parts of the image differently. For a given level of color noise, you might get rich color in the bright objects, but poor color in the dim areas. Driving down color noise will give you better color in the dimmer portions of the image.

You can avoid weak color in dim areas by applying the same exposure rules to color frames that you apply to luminance frames.

Just as you would find an optimal exposure time for luminance that swamps read noise with shot noise, you should do the same for your individual color exposures. And you should also accumulate long total exposure times to reduce noise in your color frames.

My rule of thumb is to accumulate a total red exposure time binned 2x2 that is roughly the same as the total luminance exposure time unbinned (1x1). (The blue and green exposure times are determined from the red using the ratios required for color balance.) This is a pretty radical increase in color exposure time for most imagers, but less exposure time gives you poor color in the dim details.

At a minimum, to get good color in the brightest objects, total red exposure time should be at least 25% of luminance.

Atmospheric Extinction

The elevation of an object affects color balance: the more atmosphere you image through, the more scattering that occurs. Shorter wavelengths (blue) are scattered more than longer (red), so imaging at lower elevations reddens your exposures.

The table below shows how to compensate your exposures for atmospheric extinction. Note that above elevations of about 45 degrees, the amount of correction even in blue is minimal. For most imagers, correction above 45 degrees is not essential. Corrections will be most valuable for values shown in bold.

Suppose that your red exposure time is 5 minutes. This might be the longest you can image without excessive blooming, or it might be your optimal individual exposure time using an exposure calculator. If your RGB exposure ratios are 1:1.2:1.5 minutes, then your base exposure times would be 5 minutes in red, 6 minutes in green, and 7.5 minutes in blue. Using the table below, the adjustments for imaging at 35 degrees above the horizon are as follows:

Red: 5 * 1.063 = 5 minutes, 20 seconds
Green: 6 * 1.125 = 6 minutes, 45 seconds
Blue: 7.5 * 1.180 = 8 minutes, 50 seconds

Elevation	Air Mass	Red correction	Green correction	Blue correction
90	1.000	1.000	1.000	1.000
80	1.015	1.001	1.002	1.003
70	1.064	1.005	1.010	1.014
60	1.155	1.013	1.025	1.035
55	1.221	1.018	1.036	1.050
50	1.305	1.025	1.050	1.070
45	1.414	1.034	1.068	**1.097**
40	1.555	1.046	**1.092**	**1.132**
35	1.743	1.063	**1.125**	**1.180**
30	2.000	1.085	**1.172**	**1.249**
25	2.365	**1.118**	**1.242**	**1.356**
20	2.923	**1.170**	**1.356**	**1.535**
15	3.862	**1.263**	**1.574**	**1.892**

Chapter 7

Image Cleanup

Image Cleanup

Objective

Remove evidence of hot pixels, cold pixels, cosmic ray hits and dust mote shadows from the image.

Techniques
- Median combine
- Cloning
- Correcting hot and cold pixels
- Sharpening and increasing contrast

Tools
- Photoshop® Dust & Scratches filter
- Unsharp masking
- Photoshop® Curves

Description

Hot/cold pixels: These show up as bright and dark pixels in your image. Single bright pixels are true hot pixels—for one reason or another, a pixel wound up with excess charge that causes it to appear brighter than it should. There is always some level of random variation (noise) in pixel brightness, but occasionally you'll get major misbehavior. Just as there can be hot (bright) pixels, there can be cold (dark) pixels, and for similar reasons. Groups of cold pixels are usually the result of cosmic ray hits (see below) in your dark frame.

Cosmic rays: Groups and streaks of bright pixels are often the result of a cosmic ray hit. The high energy of the cosmic ray kicks out extra electrons in the pixels that the ray moves through. Sometimes, a cosmic ray hit can mimic the appearance of a star. If you see a star in only one image, chances are it isn't a star at all, just a straight-on cosmic ray.

Dust mote shadows: Dust on optical surfaces will cast shadows. If the sky background or object is bright enough, you'll see the shadows in your image.

Definitions

Cloning: Using the Photoshop® Clone tool to copy one part of an image to another part. This is usually done to remove a defect of some kind by covering it up using an exact copy of an area of the image with similar brightness.

Dark frame: An exposure taken with the shutter closed. A dark frame is subtracted from a light frame to remove instrument artifacts (thermal current).

Dust mote: A bit of dust—perhaps even too small to see without a magnifying glass and strong light—on an optical surface. Dust motes are a concern because of the shadows they cast onto the CCD chip.

Healing brush: A type of cloning tool that does not simply copy one part of the image over another. It mixes the existing brightness of the target region with the texture of the source region to clean up imperfections.

Histogram: A graph that shows the relative number of pixels at each brightness value. The greater the number of pixels at a given brightness level, the higher the peak on the graph. Both linear and non-linear changes affect the histogram.

Light frame: A normal exposure with the shutter open.

Linear: Brightness and Contrast adjustments that preserve the internal brightness relationships of the image.

Mean combine: Also called an Average combine. Uses a simple arithmetic mean of the pixel values in each image to create a combined result. Very effective at reducing noise,

but not very good at removing outlier pixels such as hot/cold pixels and cosmic rays.

Median combine: A type of image stacking that is especially effective at removing outliers, such as random hot and cold pixels or groups of pixels caused by cosmic ray hits. However, a Median combine results in a noisier background than a Mean combine.

Non-linear: Brightness and Contrast adjustments that do not preserve internal brightness relationships. One part of the image might get a large boost, while another part might get only a small boost, or even a reduction, in brightness.

Outlier: A value that is markedly larger or smaller than typical. In the set 100, 101, 93, 421, the value "421" is an outlier. In an image, an outlier is usually caused by things like hot pixels, cosmic ray hits, and satellite trails. Using the appropriate combine method, an outlier becomes a removable error.

Points: Added to the Curves dialog to control how much boost or cut each brightness range in the image receives.

Statistical combine: There are more sophisticated combine methods that take the best of Mean and Median combine methods. They typically remove outliers, and then perform a Mean combine.

Thermal noise: Electrons that leak into a pixel during an exposure. A dark frame records the thermal noise so it can be subtracted from a light frame.

Unsharp mask: A type of sharpening that is especially effective for astronomical images.

Photoshop® (and Other) Tips

NOTE: This set of tips includes one tip (Combine Methods) that happens before you bring an image into Photoshop®.

Combine Methods

Before you bring an image into Photoshop®, you will typically take multiple exposures and combine them using other programs such as CCDStack, CCDSoft or MaxIm DL. These are programs with specialized image processing features for CCD imagers.

Photoshop® layers aren't sophisticated enough for combining astronomical images. Specialized software offers combine methods that range from simply averaging the images together to using fancy statistical combine methods.

The two most commonly used combine methods are mean (average) and median.

Mean combine: The image at right shows the result of a mean (average) combine. Many outliers remain after

using a Mean combine. The arrows point to a few of the many hot pixels, and the circles enclose some cosmic ray hits.

Mean calculates the average of the same pixel in each image. For example, if the brightness of a given pixel in five different images is 1054, 1101, 1092, 1104, and 1088, then the average brightness is 1087.8.

All of the pixel values are used to calculate the result, so outliers can be a problem. Suppose one of the images has a cosmic ray hit at this pixel location. The five values might then be

42935, 1101, 1092, 1104, and 1088. The average of these values is 9464. The outlier's high value skews the average dramatically. This means that the outlier pixels persist through the averaging process.

Median combine: Calculates the median value of the pixels in the individual images. Using the same values from the previous example, the median value is the one in the middle, or 1092. This is true whether one of the pixels is 1054 or 42935.

As a result, in the image at right, the cosmic ray hits are nowhere to be seen, though a few hot pixels remain (arrows).

Flaws that affect only one image do not persist through a median combine. The individual images were guided, so the hot pixels remained at exactly the same location. This enabled them to persist through the median combine.

❧ TIP: You can make median combine more effective at removing hot pixels by imaging unguided, or by using dithering (guide star offsets).

Statistical combine: Averaging results in the lowest noise, and median removes outliers. It would seem that a technique that combines both approaches would be ideal: remove the outliers, and then average what's left.

Programs such as CCDStack (from CCDWare) and Ray Gralak's Sigma Combine do just that, often including multiple methods for removing those outliers. You'll learn more about statistical combine methods later in this chapter.

Cloning and Healing

Cloning is the astrophotographer's friend. The Cloning tool cleans up small flaws effectively. Alt click to pick up a sample from the image, then left click to drop it on a flaw (see at right).

ᴥ Tɪᴘ: Cloning makes an exact copy. It's critical to pick up from an area with similar brightness and texture.

The Cloning tool deposits an exact copy of the sample. The Healing brush, on the other hand, merges the sample into the target, adjusting brightness and texture.

ᴥ Tɪᴘ: When you use the Healing brush, it might temporarily look like a disaster. Photoshop® might

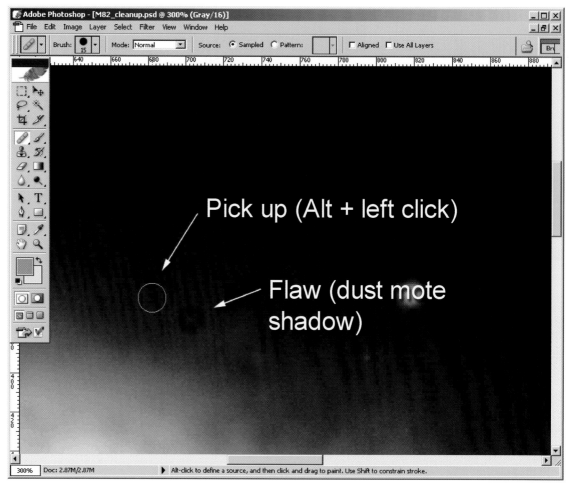

take a moment to calculate the final result. Don't panic! The Healing brush also misbehaves near stars. If you try to heal a flaw near a star, the healing might be brighter than the surrounding background. The Cloning tool is a better choice

near stars, and the Healing brush is the best tool just about everywhere else. You can use this file from the DVD to practice cloning, healing, and using the Dust & Scratches filter:

\C7\M82_cleanup.psd

Random Pixels

Some CCD chips have more random pixel variations than others. When you combine using a Mean combine, you'll see a large number of hot and cold pixels. When you subtract a dark from a light frame, you'll get hot and cold pixels from both types of frames.

When faced with this problem, you really need to use both of the available techniques for dealing with hot and cold pixels:

- Use unguided or dithered exposures so that the troublesome pixels aren't always in the same place in each image. This means that, typically, you will only have one outlier at any given pixel position because you are shifting the outliers (hot and cold pixels) around.

- Use statistical combine methods to remove the outliers

❧ TIP: Although I am discussing this in the context of CCD chips with higher than average numbers of hot pixels, you can improve your results with almost any CCD camera using dithering and statistical combine methods. The improvement won't be as dramatic, but you will in fact get cleaner (lower noise) combined images.

Russell Croman's software, the RC-Astro Processing Console (see screen capture at upper right), is free software that includes a statistical combine method called Sigma-Reject. You can download and learn more about the software here:

http://www.rc-astro.com/resources/rc_console.html

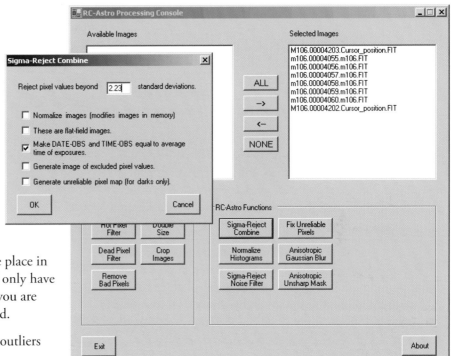

You could also clean up random pixels with the Photoshop® Dust & Scratches filter, but that can have unwanted side effects, such as elimination of dim stars from the image. Statistical combine methods are more effective and do very little collateral damage.

NOTE: If you see multi-pixel vertical or horizontal "hot pixels," that is probably not actually a hot-pixel problem. It could be that the camera's voltage is too high or too low. A new power supply might solve the problem. If not, you should have the camera serviced.

Why Combine Statistically?

If you haven't studied statistics, and that describes most of us, why should you put in the effort to learn about statistical combine methods? The answer is pretty simple: the results speak for themselves.

In the preceding pages, it's obvious that the hot pixels, cosmic ray hits, and other outliers are dealt with effectively. But you could also use the Clone tool to clean them up. There is actually much more behind the concept of outliers than the obvious.

Every pixel in your combined image gets the benefit of using statistical techniques to find and remove outliers. An outlier that is 10000 units brighter than its surroundings obviously must go. But what about an outlier that is merely 25 units brighter? If you learn how to adjust the settings in your software, you can tune it to handle even minor outliers.

An image can easily have thousands and thousands of such minor outliers. They reduce contrast, introduce false details, and are a major contributor of noise in general. By removing these minor outliers, you are improving many more pixels in the image than the obvious problems you can see.

You'll get smoother backgrounds, and the ability to dig deeper into the image for faint details, when you take advantage of the benefits that statistical combine methods offer.

CCDStack for Data Rejection

CCDStack takes statistical combining to a completely new level. First, it separates data rejection from the combine step. So we'll be talking about data rejection in this section, not statistical combining. After all, the goal of any statistical combine is to reject the bad data. Second, it offers a wide range of statistical tools to figure out what data to reject.

In other words, first reject the outliers, then combine using only the good data. (CCDStack keeps track of the good and bad values for you.)

NOTE: CCDStack also breaks down the other key steps in image processing to their fundamentals. This makes it an ideal software package for the serious imager who wants to gain the greatest degree of control over all aspects of image processing prior to adjustments in Photoshop®.

A typical session in CCDStack involves a stack of images, usually 7–10 or more. Because data rejection involves removing outliers, it is necessary to have a large enough sample to generate an accurate result. If you start with seven images, and two pixel values are rejected, that leaves five for combining. If you start with three or four images, rejection is not only less accurate, you have very few pixels left to perform calculations on. The more images, the better, when it comes to statistical image processing.

The typical workflow in CCDStack is:

Load images » Calibrate » Align » Normalize » Data Reject » Mean Combine » Save FITS » Apply DDP » Save JPG

The screen capture shown at right illustrates a typical data rejection step in CCDStack. The stack of images is shown in the window at top left, with important details about each image shown. The small control at top right moves from one image to another.

The chosen data rejection method is STD Sigma Reject. Many others are also available (Poisson sigma reject, linear factor reject, clip min/max, and reject hot/cold pixels, to name a few).

STD Sigma Reject removes outliers using a formula. It looks for pixels that are outside the bounds of the formula, and removes the worst outlier. It then repeats the formula, and continues until all outliers are removed. This rejection method requires at least 8–10 images to be effective. The formula is:

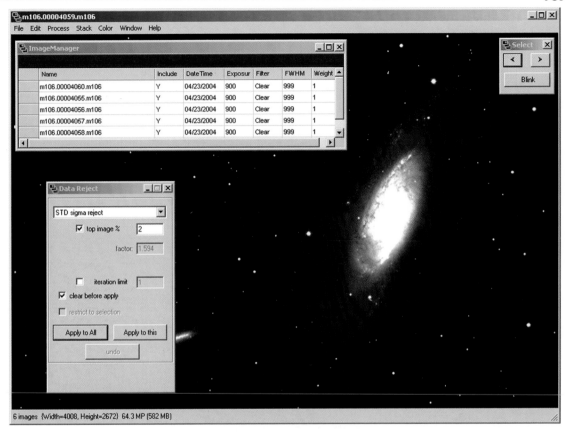

*mean ± (SD * multiplier)*

Where SD is the standard deviation of the sample. In plain English, pixel values that are greater or smaller than the mean by (standard deviation times some multiplier) are rejected.

In this example, the multiplier is called factor, and it is set to 1.594. You can test various multipliers using a small area of the image, or you can simply specify a rejection percentage for the top image, and allow CCDStack to estimate the factor (multiplier) for you. For most images, a rejection percentage of 2.0% is appropriate. Smaller values might not clean up the image adequately, while larger values can wind up removing valid data.

Soft Stars

Unless you are imaging on a mountain peak with superb seeing, and unless you have optics of space-telescope quality, your stars will have soft edges most of the time. And the harder you work with Photoshop® Curves to bring out faint details, the more you will reveal faint halos around stars.

In addition to the obvious effects of seeing, other factors can conspire to mess up your stars. A mirror with a turned edge, for example, will create diffraction spikes around bright stars. The image of the Galactic Wanderer at right shows an example of this effect. (A turned edge is a very slight downward curve at the outside edge of a mirror.)

The medium-bright stars are also affected by the turned edge; they have a soft halo surrounding them.

The stars that result from a turned edge are often called "hairy stars" and it is not good news to find out you have this problem!

There are other causes of soft stars, and the result is the same: they make an image look less attractive.

There are two types of cures for soft stars: changes to your hardware, and image processing tricks. Hardware changes range from better focusing to a mask for a turned edge. The two most common image processing tricks both involve contrast enhancement:

Histogram manipulation: Using Curves, you can increase the contrast of the stars from center to edge.

Sharpening: Sharpening takes place mostly at the edge between the star and the background.

❧ TIP: In order to work on the stars, you must first select them and paste a copy into a new layer. Please see chapter 5, *Selecting Stars,* for details.

Image processing tricks can't completely clean up soft stars. The best answer will always be high optical quality. However, even excellent optics under superb seeing will not give you perfect stars—the atmosphere will always contribute some degree of softness to the star images. Almost any image can benefit from some processing of the stars. As a result, the techniques in this chapter have become part of my standard processing for all images.

The image at right on this page shows soft stars that are a result of several problems. The Schmidt-Cassegrain optics were about average; seeing conditions were decent but not great; and the filters used were later found to have a rough surface that scattered light. Despite these obstacles, the image is a deep one, but the stars are on the soft side.

❧ TIP: One of the most common causes of stars being softer than they need to be is not-quite-perfect focus. It's worth some time to learn what good focus looks like with your equipment and with the range of seeing conditions you typically encounter at your usual imaging location.

There is also some vertical elongation of the stars, especially at the top of the image. This is the result of collimation not being spot on.

The image at right shows how the stars have been firmed up using the techniques described in this chapter. The downside is that the processing choices emphasize the vertical elongation of the stars. The more you learn about image processing, the more you learn about the flaws in your equipment and your imaging technique!

For information on fixing up elongated stars, see chapter 8, *Fixing Star Elongation.*

The bulk of the stars constitute the brightest part of the Bright Zone. Selecting the stars and working on them separately is a form of subzonal processing.

❧ Tip: Use a very light unsharp mask to sharpen up the dimmest stars. Use a very mild Gaussian blur on the darkest parts of the background afterwards to clean up if needed.

Cleaning Up Soft Stars

Use the following file from the DVD to work along with this exercise:

> *If you would like to follow along with this exercise, open the following file from the DVD in Photoshop® CS (or later):*
>
> \C7\M82_clean2.psd

This is a cleaned-up version of the file used to demonstrate the Cloning and Healing techniques shown earlier in this chapter, and it includes star selections listed below. A version without selections is also available if you want to create them yourself:

   \C7\M82_clean.psd

Stars Raw: Stars as selected using the techniques described in chapter 5.

Stars Feathered: The Raw selection was expanded by 6 pixels and feathered by 3 pixels.

Stars Tight: The Feathered selection was contracted by 5 pixels.

The Feathered selection is used when working with Curves to increase star edge contrast. The Tight selection is used when sharpening. If you are working with the **M82_clean.psd** file and creating your own stars selections, be sure to create these three selections before continuing with the exercise.

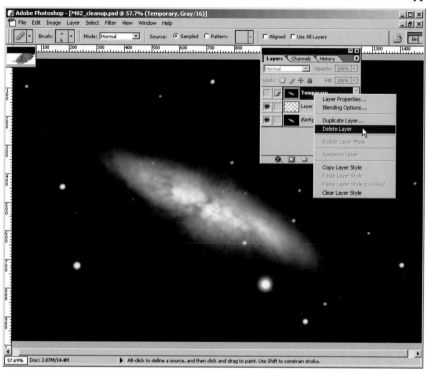

TIP: Why two selections? The Feathered selection includes a significant portion of the background, and is useful for controlling how the star blends into the background. The Tight selection eliminates most (but not all!) of the background, and is much easier to work with when using Unsharp Masking or the Minimum filter.

The amount by which the Raw selection was expanded, feathered, and contracted depends on the image. The numbers used here are good for this image, but you might need larger or smaller numbers for any given image.

Once you have created your selections, highlight the layer containing the stars in the Layers palette. Open Curves and create a curve like the one shown at right.

For the Standard Curve, you added the first point on the left (Dim Zone) and worked toward the Bright Zone. For stars, start with the point on the right, and work back toward the Dim Zone.

Add the first point about 75% of the way toward the upper right corner. Drag that point upwards and observe what happens to the stars in the image. The bright star core expands when you increase contrast—the core now makes up a larger portion of the star.

Now add a second point at about the 50% portion of the Curve. Drag this second point downward, and observe what happens: the edge of the star becomes firmer.

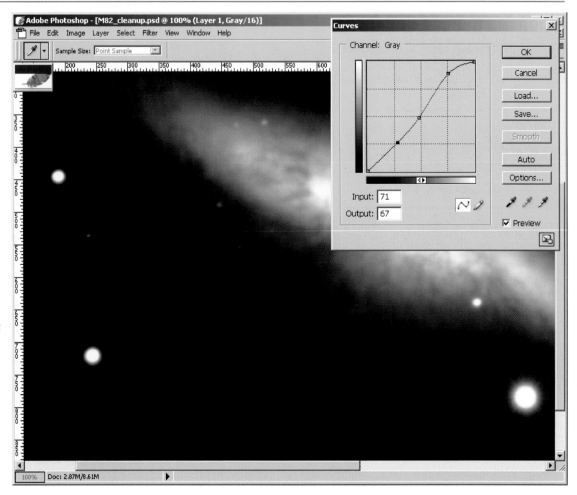

The third point must match the brightness of the area around the star. The goal is to position this point so that the fringe of the star matches the background level. You can click just outside the star to see where the background brightness sits on the Curve. That is where you want to add your point to control the brightness of the edge of the star.

ॐ Tɪᴘ: The 50% and 75% locations for the points are not absolute. They work well for this image. But you might find times where you want to vary the points left or right to get the best possible result. Use the standard locations when you are starting out, and experiment to get the best match between the edge of the star and the background.

The general shape of the curve shown on the previous page is typical for fixing up soft or bloated stars: push the curve up at the top right, down in the middle, and make a straight diagonal (45 degrees) at bottom left. It is an inverse of the Standard Curve. This curve emphasizes the Bright Zone, while the standard curve emphasizes the Dim Zone.

Experiment with the placement of the 50% and 75% points. Try moving them up and down as a first step in your experimentation. Moving the 75% point up will make the star appear to grow in size; this is a side effect of this process. You might have to allow some level of growth to get a cleaner star profile. Lower the 50% point to control this growth. You can only control it so much, however. Trying to over-control the growth of the star from this process will lead to excessive darkening in the halo around the star. You can limit the dark halo by careful adjustment of that third point. Use the third point to match the outer fringe of the star to the brightness of the area around the star.

If you have different brightness levels behind different stars—stars in front of a galaxy or nebula are the most common cause—you will need different curves in different parts of the image. Create separate selections based on background brightness, and use different curves on each selection.

Unsharp Mask

If the stars still look soft after applying Curves in the manner described here, you can use an Unsharp Mask to further define the edges of the stars. There are some general rules to follow for best results:

Use a large Amount setting: For most sharpening, I recommend keeping the Amount value at 50%. This blends the sharpening with the original image to limit artifacts. For stars, an amount in the 60-80% range might be more effective. After all, the goal here is to increase contrast, not smooth it out!

Use a non-zero Threshold value: We want to sharpen the star as a whole, not the pixels that make it up. A higher threshold value ignores small details, and emphasizes large details (like stars). A threshold setting of 2 to 5 should work for most situations. The longer your focal length, and the smaller your pixels, the more likely you will benefit from a larger threshold setting. Normally, it is rare to use a threshold value higher than 2, but stars are an exception.

Match Radius to Threshold: Use a radius value that is equal to or larger than the Threshold value.

As always, keep an eye on the darkening of the halo around the star. You might need to go back to Curves after unsharp masking in order to fix up such darkening.

ॐ Tɪᴘ: Use a fairly tight selection for sharpening. Otherwise, you can wind up with a fringe of high-contrast pixels around the star. You can use History to undo your sharpening, or you can blur the noisy pixels around the star using the Blur tool.

The image at right shows typical Unsharp Mask settings for firming up the edge of stars. The Amount is a little larger than usual, 60%. The Threshold has been set to 3 (4 might also work well for this image). And the Radius is a bit larger than the threshold: 3.6.

For badly bloated stars, you might wind up with settings of 80% for the Amount, 5-7 for the Radius, and a Threshold of 4 or 5.

It's not a bad idea to see what you can get by being very aggressive with sharpening. The high threshold value will protect the image from serious artifacts. You might want to start with very aggressive settings, and throttle them back until you get the effect you want.

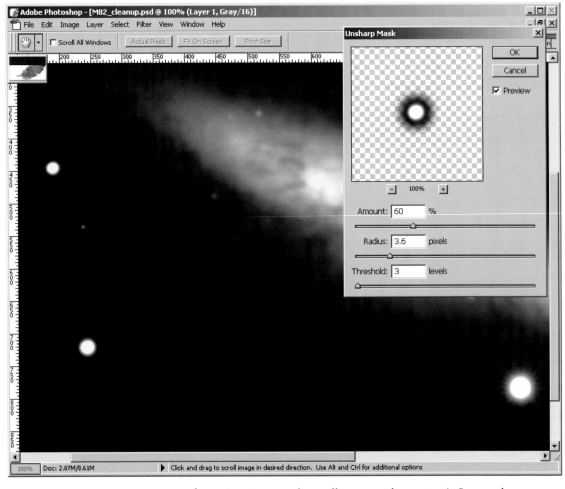

With three settings that interact (Amount, Threshold, Radius), it can be difficult to know which to change when. I would recommend that you keep the Threshold high; only lower it if necessary to get more sharpening (if it is too high for a given image, that will prevent sharpening). Lower the Radius next, and finally the Amount. Don't lower just one of them dramatically; if you find a need for a large reduction, reduce all three values together and then assess the results. Excessive star sharpening almost always creates a dark halo.

Minimum Filter

After increasing contrast with Curves, and maybe even after applying an Unsharp mask, your stars might still be too big for your taste. The seeing might have been bad, or your focus might have been out a bit, or you might simply be over sampled (i.e., pixels too small for the seeing conditions). Whatever the cause, you might be able to use the Minimum filter to reduce the size of the stars.

I previously pointed out that increasing star contrast tends to grow the stars a bit. This growth occurs because you are brightening the soft, fuzzy portion of the star to firm up the edge. In other words, the star always was this big, now it is simply more obvious. You can try to use the Minimum filter after applying Curves to get the stars back to where they started out, and sometimes to even make an improvement.

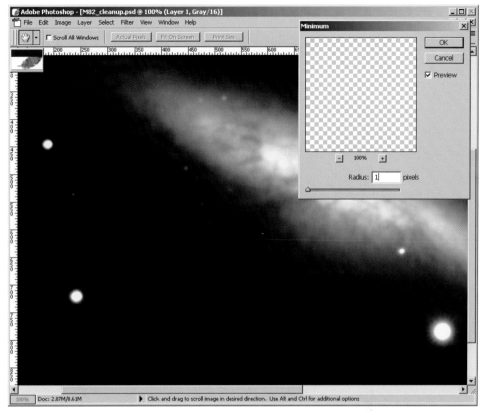

The least aggressive Radius setting, a value of 1, has a dramatic effect. You will rarely be able to use a setting larger than 1 because it will either distort the stars, or eliminate the dim and medium stars.

As is often the case, the Minimum filter reveals some of the more subtle issues in the image (see above). The smaller stars show elongation. (The larger stars are big enough to mask a pixel or two of elongation.)

Chapter 8, *Fixing Star Elongation,* shows you how to deal with this problem—create a new layer, set the blend mode to darken, and then use the Offset filter to shift the image, and the *Edit » Fade Offset* menu item to do sub-pixel adjustments.

☙ Tip: You can also get sub-pixel results by enlarging the image, applying the filter, then reducing the image. This can soften the image, however. Use only enlargements of 100% (half pixel), 200% (one-third pixel), etc.

❧ Tip: You can also use the *Edit» Fade Minimum* menu item to do subpixel Minimum filters. You must always use *Edit» Fade <most recent filter>* immediately after applying the filter. The menu item is not available after you perform any other actions in Photoshop®.

The sequence at the bottom of this page shows what happens to the star at lower left on the previous image as you apply the various steps outlined in this exercise.

1. Original appearance

2. Appearance after an application of Curves. The star core appears larger, and the width of the halo around the star is greatly reduced. For many images, this is as far as you have to go. The additional steps are for dealing with problems that might show up from time to time.

3. Appearance after Unsharp Masking. The edge is firmer, but somewhat ragged. Always remember to contract the selection around the star before you sharpen!

4. Appearance after applying a Minimum filter with a radius of 2 pixels. The star is slightly elongated horizontally, and shows just a bit of squaring from diffraction effects that were too weak to be visible prior to this step. A Minimum filter exaggerates any kind of diffraction effect, from the large spikes you get with a spider to subtle effects like these. Even refractors will show diffraction effects, such as from small clips used to hold the objective in its cell. Depending on what the Minimum filter reveals, you might or might not be able to use it. Or you might need to use *Edit» Fade Minimum* to reduce artifacts.

5. Appearance after applying an Offset filter to get rid of the slight elongation.

6. Appearance after applying Fade Offset to achieve a sub-pixel offset and a rounder star.

❧ Tip: You might find that stars of different sizes might require different amounts of effort. For example, you might wind up applying a second Curve to further enhance the edges of the larger stars. You can do this right after step #2, or sometimes even after you use sharpening or a Minimum filter. If sharpening of the Minimum filter darkens the halo around the star, you might need to use another application of Curves.

But wait! There's more! The large stars are OK now, and the stars against the background are also looking much better. But the stars in front of the galaxy might show signs of trouble. It is common for the stars in front of a bright background to need some special treatment.

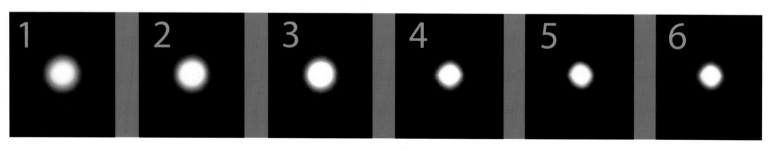

Fixing Star Halos

The stars in front of any bright object (e.g., galaxy or nebula) often need special treatment. One solution is to handle these the same way you handle bigger and smaller stars: create separate layers. For an image like this one, you can create one layer for the stars over the galaxy, and another for stars against the background.

❧ Tɪᴘ: Be sure to include stars that are in front of the faint portions of the galaxy. As shown in the image at right, even a little bit of background brightness can create trouble. If necessary, create two layers: one for the bright portions of the galaxy, and one for the dim portions.

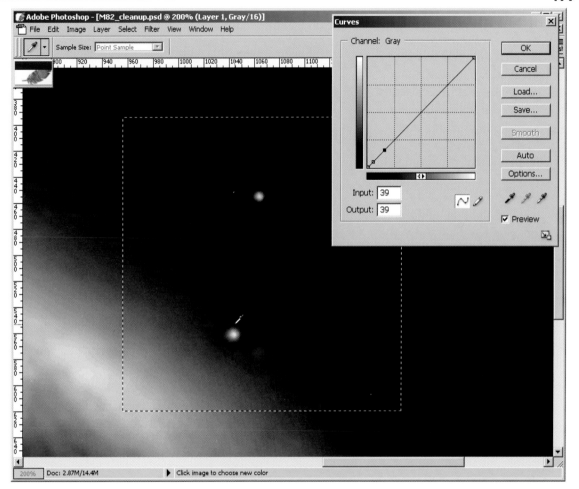

The typical outcome of fussing with the stars is to wind up with a dark halo in front of bright objects. You can use selections and Curves to fix this. In the image above, two stars are in the selection, and two points have been added to the curve. Both points were added by holding down the Control key and clicking in the middle of the dark halo around the star. The two points correspond to the two star halos. The point at lower left is from the halo of the star just barely against the galaxy's background. The other point is from the star closer to the galaxy's core.

NOTE: The layer with the stars has not yet been merged with the background. Only merge the stars back into the main image when you need to make adjustments with Levels or Curves to both layers at the same time. Until that becomes necessary, and especially until you have resolved all of the problems and issues in the stars layer, keep them separate. You never know when you'll need to operate on the stars!

❧ TIP: Save your selections as you work in case you need them again. This is especially important for the stars because the selections are typically complex.

Since each point corresponds to a star, you can move the points upward to adjust until the halos match the galaxy in the background. If you

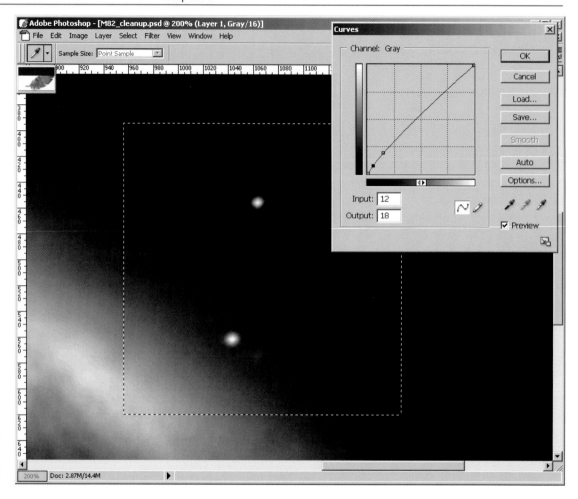

have lots of stars in this condition, you might have to work carefully to find a curve that will make them all look OK. If you can't manage that, you might need to divide the stars into separate layers based on the brightness of the background. Ad-

just each layer individually, with a curve that fits the brightness of the star halo to the brightness of the background. The power of this approach is limited only by your patience. A light Gaussian blur, or an application of the Blur tool, will correct the darkest spots in the halos. (These are artifacts of

Fixing Star Elongation

Clean Up Star Elongation/Reduce Bloated Stars

Objective

Turn elongated stars into round stars.

Techniques
- Select stars (see chapter 5)
- Use the Darken blend mode
- Use the Offset filter
- *Edit»Fade* to control amount of offset
- Reduce star size
- Scale transformation

Tools
- Photoshop® Layers Palette
- Photoshop® Filters: Offset, Minimum
- Photoshop® Unsharp Mask with non-zero threshold

Description

There are many things that can lead to elongated stars, from collimation problems to poor guiding. Elongated stars have a serious negative impact on the image, and an ability to clean them up is a valuable asset.

Start by creating a layer with just the stars in it using the techniques in chapter 5. Photoshop® blend modes give you the key tool to correct the elongation. The blend modes offer different rules for how to blend two images. In this chapter, you'll use the Darken blend mode. The rule for the Darken blend mode is simple: the darkest pixel always wins. By offsetting a copy of the stars, you move darker pixels over the underlying copy, and since the darker pixel wins, you neatly round up the stars.

Definitions

Collimation: When an optical system's elements are all properly lined up, they are said to be collimated. Some telescope types, such as refractors, hold collimation well and might not need field collimation. Other types of telescopes, such as Newtonians and Cassegrains, might need frequent collimation. Not only will collimation improve optical performance, but it will help you get round stars in your images.

Curves: A Photoshop® tool for making non-linear adjustments to the image's histogram. There is a tendency to think of Curves only for overall image manipulation, but in this chapter you'll learn a method for applying Curves to stars.

Darken blend mode: A blend mode where the darkest pixel is the one that is displayed. Used in this chapter to remove star elongation.

Elongation: A star image that is longer in one direction than in others. Elongation most often occurs when guiding cannot keep up with perturbations, such as when wind jostles the mount along a specific axis. But it can also occur from optical effects such as coma, tilted optical elements, and even from collimation error.

Fade: After using a filter, you have the option of fading the filter effect from 1–100%. This is especially useful when you are dealing with filters that have a large minimum adjustment (such as the Minimum filter's radius of one full pixel). Note that you *must* use the Fade option *immediately* after applying a filter.

Layer: A Photoshop® file can have more than one layer. You can perform interesting operations between layers using blend modes. For astronomical image processing, layers allow you to do things like fix up problems with stars, and achieve different color balance for different types of objects.

Minimum filter: A filter often used to shrink bloated stars. The Minimum filter works by comparing a given pixel to surrounding pixels—it sets a new value based on the minimum of the surrounding values. The overall effect is to shrink stars to a smaller diameter.

Offset filter: A Photoshop® filter that allows you to shift one image relative to another. You can also shift images using the Move tool, but if you use the Offset filter, you can then use the *Edit»Fade* menu item to get sub-pixel results. Normally, Photoshop® only does whole-pixel operations.

Opacity: A setting which determines how transparent a layer is. Can be used to blend layers (or versions of an image or portion of an image) using a percentage of each. For example, if the top layer has its opacity set to 30%, then it contributes 30% to what you see, and the underlying layers contribute the other 70%.

Radial elongation: When elongation occurs from mechanical problems, all stars usually elongate in the same direction. Radial elongation occurs from problems such as poor collimation or coma.

Scale: To change the size of a layer or image. Can be used to vary the amount of correction across an image or selection when used in conjunction with the Darken blend mode.

Photoshop® Tips

The key to rounding up elongated stars is using the Darken blend mode on a copy of a layer.

Layers

Photoshop® allows you to stack images on top of each other in layers. The Layers Palette (shown at right) determines how the images are stacked. You can also apply changes to individual layers, merge layers, and blend layers in various ways.

Photoshop® CS (version 8) gives you the ability for the first time to create layers in 16-bit images. The images taken with the vast majority of CCD cameras are 16-bit, which means that every pixel has more than 65,000 possible brightness values. In previous versions of Photoshop®, only 8-bit images could contain layers. An 8-bit image has a mere 256 brightness levels, a tiny fraction of what a 16-bit image contains. This support for layers in 16-bit images is one of the most important features of Photoshop® CS for astro imagers.

Photoshop® displays the combination of all layers automatically, so you are always working with a real-time display of a multi-layered image. In this tutorial, the original image will be in one layer, while a second layer is used to hold a copy of just the stars in the image. By using Blend Modes (Darken in this example), you can control how the layers combine with each other, and thus how the final image appears.

Since the final image is the combination of all the layers, you need a way to turn individual layers on and off. Sometimes

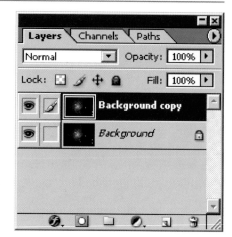

you will create layers for a specific purpose and then delete them (see chapter 5, *Selecting Stars,* for an example). At other times you will create layers that affect other layers. And in some cases you will use a layer to perform an operation on a specific zone in the image.

There are two layers shown in the sample Layers palette above: the *Background* layer and the *Background copy* layer.

☜ Tip: The copy is the result of a layer duplication. To duplicate a layer, right click the layer name and choose Duplicate Layer.

☜ Tip: To display the Layers Palette (or any other palette), use the Window menu, and click on the palette you wish to display.

From left to right, there are four items for each layer:

The eyeball: Click here to hide/show a layer.

The brush and chain: The layer with a brush is the active layer for editing, applying filters, changing blend mode, etc. A layer with a chain is linked to the current layer, and will move with it.

The preview: A thumbnail of the layer's contents.

The layer name: Displays the name of the layer, and provides information about any layer formatting (e.g., drop shadows). Layer formatting is rarely, if ever, used in astro imaging. The name of the active layer is highlighted. In this example, the layer named "Background copy" is active. All editing and filters apply to the active layer. If a filter does not do what you expected, check to see if the correct layer is active.

☜ TIP: In Photoshop® CS2, the layers palette does not include the brush-and-chain boxes. Instead, the current layer is highlighted, and you select multiple layers using Shift + Click.

The top of the Layers Palette includes tools for selecting a layer's blend mode, setting opacity percentage, locking features, and setting fill percentage.

Blend mode: Photoshop® offers many ways to blend layers. The default is the Normal blend mode, where layers stack on top of each other. Transparent portions of one layer allow underlying layers to show through. Unless you choose a different blend mode, the top layer always "wins" the battle to be seen.

Opacity: By changing the opacity of a layer, you control whether underlying layers show through it. For example, you can use layers to do a type of Fade (see *Fade Tool* later in this chapter). Let's suppose you sharpen a layer, and that the sharpened layer is above the original layer. You could set the blend mode of the sharpened layer to 50%, and the result will be an equal combination of the two layers.

Lock icons: These control locking of Transparency, Editing, Position, and All, respectively. You can lock a layer or some aspects of the layer to prevent an unwanted change later on.

Fill opacity: Controls the opacity of pixels painted onto a layer. This is seldom used in astro imaging.

Layers are one of the most powerful features of Photoshop®. For example, you can select the stars in an image, paste the stars into a new layer, and then operate on the stars without affecting other parts of the image. Stars are mostly in the Bright zone of the image, and thus can be sharpened without ill effects to the other zones in the image.

With most of the image processing programs available for CCD imaging, you must apply a filter to the entire image. In Photoshop®, using layers and selections, you can apply filters only to the zone or sub-zone that will benefit from the filter.

Selections are a valuable tool for working with layers. The case of selecting just the stars in an image is one example. You can select any zone in the image and convert it to a layer. To turn a selection into a layer: make the selection, verify that the source layer is the active layer, and copy to the clipboard (*Edit » Copy*). Now paste the clipboard into the image, and Photoshop® creates a new layer.

☜ TIP: You can right click on a layer and choose Layer Properties to rename the layer.

☜ TIP: After working in separate layers, it is sometimes necessary to merge the layers back together. To merge only certain layers, click in the brush/chain area and a chain link appears. You can then merge the linked layers with the *Layer » Merge Linked* menu item. In Photoshop® CS2, select multiple layers using Shift + Click.

Darken Blend Mode

Access Blend modes in the Layers Palette and in many Photoshop® dialogs and tools.

Darken is just one of many blend modes available on the Layers palette. Blend modes aren't only available on the Layers palette. Many other tools offer some or all of the blend modes as an option. For example, when you apply a Fade, you can use a Blend mode to control how the fade is applied.

Blend modes control how a layer combines with the layers below it. In the Normal mode, the pixels in the upper layer "win" and are displayed. The other blend modes offer alternative rules to determine which pixel (or some combination of the pixels in the two layers) wins.

The Darken blend mode uses a very simple rule: the darker pixel always wins. If the darker pixel is in the underlying layer, then the pixel value from the underlying layer is displayed. Likewise, if the darker pixel is in the upper layer, that is the pixel that is displayed at that location.

As you might imagine, the Lighten blend mode does the opposite—the brighter pixel wins.

The Darken blend mode is used for fixing up elongated stars. You will use the Offset filter to move some background pixels over part of the bright, elongated portion of the star. The darker pixels win, and hide the unwanted bright portion of the star. Since the hiding is done with existing background pixels, the result looks very clean and natural.

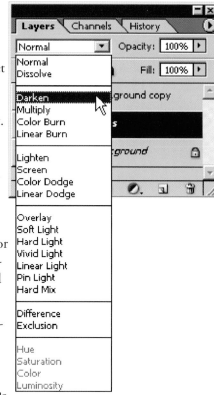

❧ TIP: Since the Darken blend mode works in conjunction with the Offset filter to make the magic happen, you can adapt the action by varying the offset. You can even use multiple offsets in a single image. For example, if collimation is off, the elongation will change direction throughout the image. By creating multiple layers, one layer for each direction, you can offset each layer in the desired direction.

Your ability to correct complex elongations is limited only by your willingness to create the necessary layers for each direction of elongation.

❧ TIP: By resizing layers instead of using the Offset filter, you can create different amounts of elongation cleanup across an image. For example, if you resize from the left side, you will have more elongation correction on the left side, and almost none on the right. You might use this for images that have more elongation on one side due to a tilted filter. The possibilities for elongation correction are limited only by your imagination and work ethic.

Offset Filter

To access the Offset filter, use the Filter»Other» Offset menu item.

The Offset filter is invaluable for fixing up stars. This is one of several filters tucked away in the "Other" section of the filters menu. The Offset filter shifts a layer (or selection) up/down and left/right.

❧ TIP: You can also move (nudge) a layer/selection by nudging with the arrow keys. Hold down the Control key while you use the arrow keys, and the current layer will move. The amount of the move depends on the current magnification level. If the magnification is 100% or more, then the move will be single pixels. If the view is zoomed out, the moves will be two or more pixels.

There is a big disadvantage to using the keyboard to nudge a layer, however: the Fade tool will not be available after a nudge. The Fade tool allows you to get sub-pixel accuracy in offsets—without the Fade tool, you can only move a layer in whole-pixel increments. With the Fade tool, you can create sub-pixel moves with high precision. Since the Fade tool is only available when you use the Offset filter, that's the only technique shown in this exercise.

❧ TIP: The Fade tool is available after you apply most types of filters. You will find it on the **Edit** menu *immediately* (and only immediately) after you apply a filter. After you move on to the next action, the Fade tool will not be available.

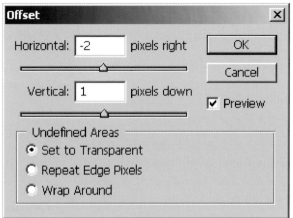

When you offset a layer, the edge pixels become undefined. On the edge where the layer is moving away, new pixels have to be created. On the edge toward which the layer is moving, pixels are lost. The Undefined Areas portion of the Offset dialog allows you to tell Photoshop® how to handle these edge situations.

For most astro images, click on *Set to Transparent*. This in effect throws away the edge pixels. The other two options lead to problems. Repeat Edge Pixels duplicates pixels as the layer moves away from the trailing edge, which would lead to elongated stars. Wrap Around moves pixels from the leading edge to the trailing edge.

Note that the horizontal movement is defined as "to the right." If you need to move to the left, use a negative number. The same applies to vertical offsets: the default is to shift down. If you need to move up, use a negative number.

❧ TIP: There is a limit to how much elongation you can fix with this technique. Moves of one or two pixels in each direction will generally look OK. Larger moves, of three of more pixels, might not look right. It's up to you to decide whether the result is good enough to salvage the image.

Fade Tool

To access Fade, use the Edit » Fade menu item.

The Fade dialog showed up a few years ago in Photoshop®, and it is a very useful tool for astro imaging.

Many Photoshop® filters operate only at the pixel level. But there are times when you really would like to perform an operation on a fraction of a pixel. For example, the Offset filter will only shift an image in whole pixels. By using the Fade tool, you can effectively offset in fractional pixels.

The Fade tool works by using an Opacity slider to determine what percentage of the filter is used. For example, if you set the Opacity to 50%, then you have effectively done one-half of the original filter. In the case of the Offset filter, that represents half a pixel of offset.

NOTE: Since the filter controls opacity, and not the actual offset, you aren't getting *exactly* a half-pixel of offset. But the effect is very close to fractional pixels, and functions with reasonable effectiveness. In most cases, you can safely use the Fade tool as if it were a fractional offset.

The Fade tool is on the *Edit* menu. It will change names depending on the filter most recently used. Always use the Fade tool immediately after using a filter, or it will be unavailable.

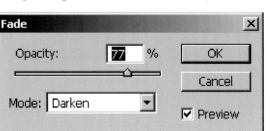

Minimum Filter

To access the Minimum filter, use the Filter » Other » Minimum menu item.

The minimum filter is useful for shrinking stars, but if it is overused it can make your images look artificial.

❧ TIP: The key to best use of the Minimum filter is to use the *Edit » Fade* menu option to cut back on the effect of the filter.

The Minimum filter has a minimum of its own: the smallest radius of operation is a full pixel. This is often too much minimizing, and that is why the Fade option is valuable. The Fade option allows you to do sub-pixel fading. That's typically the right choice for most stars in most images.

There is an exception to the need for sub-pixel minimums: fixing bloated stars. If you have bad seeing, all stars get fatter, but bright stars especially so. You might even need a 2-pixel Minimum filter for the largest stars. Make sure you select only those extra-fat stars; use a regular Minimum filter or Minimum filter plus Fade for the medium-bright stars.

Typically, you'll use a fade of 50–75% after applying a one-pixel Minimum filter.

❧ TIP: To select only the brightest stars, complete the Color Range as usual, and then use a *Select » Modify » Contract* of 1–3 pixels to eliminate the dimmest stars from the selection. Then use *Select » Modify » Enlarge* with a large enough value to re-select the remaining large stars. A value of 5–7 is typical.

Scale Transformation

To access Scaling, use the Edit» Transform» Scale menu item.

Scaling allows you to modify the size of a layer. Scaling is not to be confused with Resizing, which affects the entire canvas and all layers that make it up. Scaling affects only the current layer.

NOTE: The Background layer cannot be scaled. If you ever need to scale a background layer, duplicate the background layer and scale the duplicate. Photoshop® CS2 allows you to right click on the background, and then choose *Layer from Background.*

Scaling is typically used in two situations for astronomical image processing: to resize a layer so that it matches the size of another layer, and in combination with the Darken blend mode to clean up special types of elongated stars.

For example, if a color (RGB) layer is a slightly different size than the lu-minance layer, you could use a scale transformation to match up the sizes of the layers. Unfortunately, *Edit» Fade* is not available after scaling.

When scaling is active, the layer that is being scaled will have an outline around it. There will be grab handles (squares) on the four sides, and at the corners.

TIP: To scale without introducing distortion, hold down the Shift key as you drag a corner handle.

Open File

> *If you would like to follow along with this exercise, open the following file from the DVD in Photoshop® CS (or later):*
>
> \C8\star_elongation_start.psd

To see the elongation clearly, magnify the window to 600%. Hold down the Ctrl key and press the plus ("+") key several times to increase magnification. To reduce magnification, hold down Ctrl and press the minus ("-") key. (You can use the numeric keypad or the regular keyboard.)

As you can see, the star is elongated. The elongation is mostly left to right, but it has a bit of upward elongation as well. This is just one star out of many in an image; it wouldn't be practical to fix the stars one at a time. What's needed is a method that will fix all of the stars at one time.

The Darken blend mode is the key. Copy the stars in the original image into a new layer. You can then shift the new layer a few pixels in the correct direction, set the Darken blend mode, and the stars will round up nicely.

NOTE: To learn how to select just the stars in an image, please see chapter 5. For this example, the star selection portion of the exercise has been omitted. Always remember to include enough background around the star for the Darken blend

mode to be effective. If you select too little of the background, it might not cover up the elongation adequately.

This technique works best for stars that are elongated by a pixel or two. Extreme elongation is harder to fix. The more you have to move (offset) the top layer, the more likely that you will introduce artifacts and distortion into the stars.

To see how the Darken blend mode works, make a copy of the background layer. Right click on the name portion of the background in the Layers palette. Click *Duplicate Layer* in the popup menu that appears. In Photoshop® CS2, choose *Layer from Background.*

❧ Tɪᴘ: This opens the New or Duplicate Layer dialog. Give the new layer an appropriate name to help you keep track of what is in which layer. As you build your layering skills, layer names will help you keep track of what you are doing.

The default name for a new layer is the name of the source layer with "copy" appended. If you make more than one copy, Photoshop® will add numbers to the names.

Photoshop® puts the new layer above the layer that you copied from (see top right). The new layer is active, as indicated by the little brush icon and/or highlighting.

❧ Tɪᴘ: You can change the position of a layer by clicking on the name and dragging it up or down in the Layers palette.

Because the default blend mode is *Normal,* the new layer's pixels are the ones that you see in the image window. Photoshop® automatically applies layer

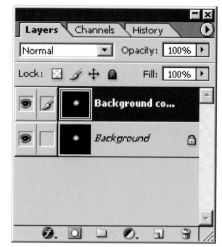

blend modes when you select one; you'll see all changes in real time. There is no need to click anything to update the display. If all blend modes are set to Normal, the topmost layer "wins" the right to display its pixels in the image window. Blend modes can interact, so you need to be careful when you select blend modes.

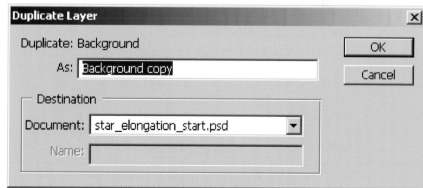

By setting a blend mode, you change the rules that govern which layer wins the battle to be seen. Photoshop® uses math to determine which pixel to display based on the blend modes of all of the layers that are present.

The Darken blend mode uses a simple rule: the darkest pixel wins the battle, no matter whether it is in the upper or lower layer.

❧ Tip: You might have guessed that you can have layers stacked on top of each layer with various blend modes. It can get challenging to keep track of what's going on when you do this, but multiple layers can be a very powerful tool. For example, you might have a luminance layer at the bottom set to Normal mode, with a stars-only layer set to Darken blend mode to correct elongation. You might then have an RGB image in the next layer above that, with the blend mode set to Color. See chapter 4 for details on the Color blend mode.

The blend modes are available in a drop-down list at the top left of the Layers palette, as shown in figure at right. The Darken blend mode is located near the top.

❧ Tip: When you select a blend mode, the focus stays in the drop-down list. If you try to use the arrow keys while the focus is still in the list, the blend mode will change. If you see weird effects in the image, it might be caused by a random blend mode. To get the focus out of the list, click on the name of the Background layer and then on the name of the layer you are working with.

When the layer is active, as shown at lower right, the blend mode of the layer automatically appears in the drop-down

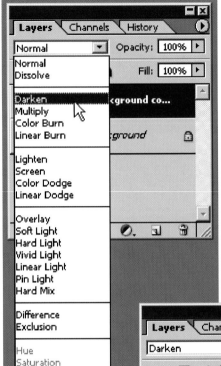

whenever that layer is the active layer.

❧ Tip: To see what effect, if any, the blend mode gives to the layer, you can click the layer on and off using the eyeball icon at the far left of the layer in the Layers palette.

We haven't made any changes to the copy layer, so there is no change if you show and hide it.

To fix star elongation, you shift the position of the copy (upper) layer so that dark pixels in the copy layer move over light pixels in the background layer. Since dark pixels win, the elongated portion of the star disappears as you make the shift.

NOTE: When you shift the star image, you are also moving light pixels over the underlying background layer. Because the dark pixels win, these light pixels do not show up in the image window. This is the magic of the Darken blend mode: you can get rid of erroneous light pixels without creating problems from the light pixels in the layer that is doing the correction.

⚜ TIP: Although you can shift a layer by holding down the Ctrl key and using the arrow keys, this is usually not the best approach. The *Edit»Fade* menu choice is only active if you use the Offset filter to do the nudging.

The shift required to fix this image is two pixels left and one pixel down. Note that the Offset dialog makes a move to the left by using –2 pixels to the right.

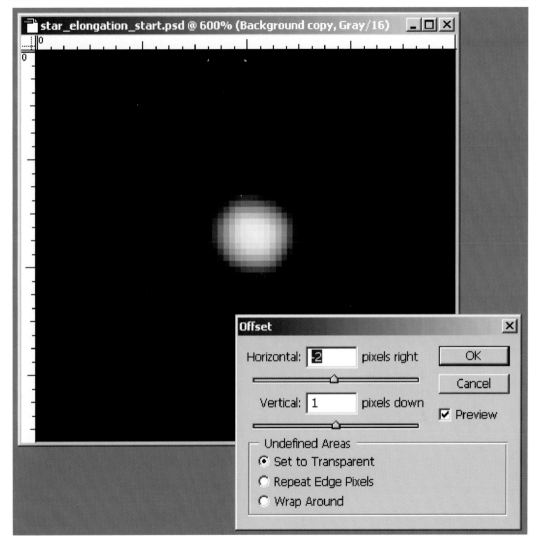

The image at right shows what has happened to the copy layer. (The Background layer is hidden because its eyeball icon has been clicked.) The copy layer has been shifted one pixel down, and two pixels to the left. The edge of the copy layer can be seen (the gray and white squares at top and right show where the copy layer has been moved away from its original position).

The copy layer still has the elongation that was present in the original; that hasn't changed at all. It is the Darken blend mode that does the work here; neither of the layers is changed in any way.

The darker pixels win, and that makes all the difference.

The files for the next exercise are on the DVD. There are two files. The .FIT file can only be opened in Photoshop® if you have a FITS plug-in installed. Otherwise, use the .PSD (native Photoshop®) version.

\C8\mice_medcomb.fit

\C8\mice_medcomb.psd

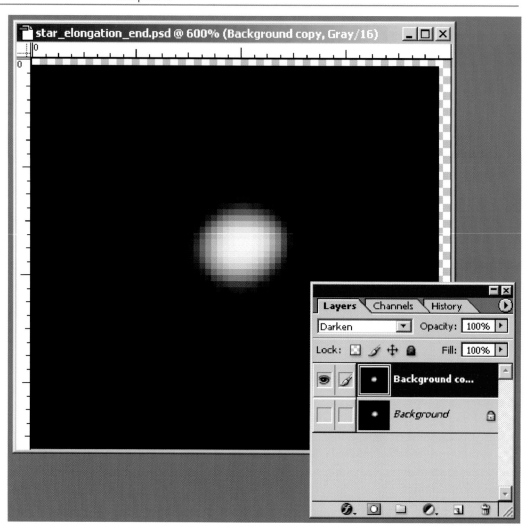

Fix Up Stars

The image of the Mice at right contains stars that are elongated, similar to what was shown in the previous example. You can open the FITS version of the image and practice basic Photoshop® processing, or you can open the PSD file and get right to fixing up the elongated stars.

NOTE: To set up for this exercise, select the stars in the Background layer as shown in chapter 5. Expand by 3 pixels, and feather by 2 pixels. Then copy the selection, and paste it in. Photoshop® will automatically create a new layer with the pasted selection in it.

mice_medcomb.psd @ 100% (Gray/16)

To view the stars layer alone, click the eyeball icon for the Background layer to hide it. You will see just the stars in the new layer, as shown on the following page.

𝕿 TIP: Right click on the name of the new layer (Layer 1 by default), click on Layer Properties, and type in the name "Stars" for the new layer. Click OK to save the change.

This is just one example of how the ability to select just the stars can be a very powerful tool. The stars occupy the very brightest values in the Bright zone, and you will often be able to clean up problems with the stars in an image if you know how to isolate them.

𝕿 TIP: You could just select the stars and then operate on them, without pasting them into a layer. But you can do more complex things to the stars if they are in a layer.

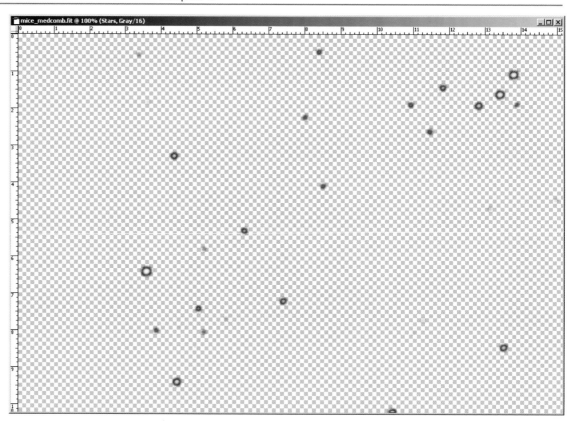

Note: The stars in the image are pretty badly elongated. Although the salvage operation improves the image, you will still see some minor flaws in the final result.

You can hide the Background layer to view the layer with stars in it, as shown at right.

As you work with stars in a layer, you might find that some changes you make affect the brightness of the darker fringes of the stars. For example, you will typically darken fringes when you sharpen the stars with an Unsharp Mask. It's easy to fix any problems of this type. Use the *Image » Adjustments » Levels* menu item to open the Levels dialog. To lighten the stars layer to match underlying layers, increase the Gamma of the stars layer (the middle slider). If you need to darken the fringes for some reason, try adjusting the black point or lowering the layer's Gamma to see which works best.

Once the Stars layer sits above the Background layer, you simply need to set the Darken blend mode, and make the same shift as in the previous example (−2 pixels right, 1 pixel down). This rounds off the stars and improves the appearance of the image.

Image shifts can only be made in whole pixel increments. Unlike many of the astronomical image processing tools, Photoshop® cannot make sub-pixel shifts. As a result, you will sometimes find yourself stuck between too little and too much correction.

The solution is to always choose the option with too much correction. When the stars are over-corrected, you can use the *Edit » Fade* menu item to reduce the effect, as shown at right. Slide the Opacity slider to the left to reduce the amount of correction. In this example, I chose to use an opacity percentage of 78. Experiment to find the value that looks best to you.

NOTE: The Fade dialog also includes blend modes. This blend mode applies only to the Fade, not the original correction, but you might find situations where the subtle effect of an additional blend mode will be helpful, so keep it in mind. When in doubt, experiment!

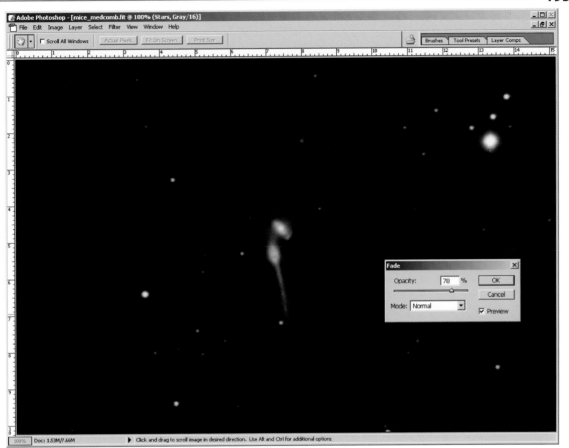

Fixing Complex Elongation Problems

In the Mice image example, elongation was the same throughout the image. The shift took care of the problem nicely. But star elongation isn't always so neat. You will see linear elongation from such things as wind, poor guiding or uncorrected periodic error. Other types of elongation can be caused by optical problems.

For example, if the CCD chip is large relative to the available flat field, the corners of the image could become elongated in a radial fashion. In such cases, the further the star is from the center of the image, the more elongation there will be.

Another problem that elongates stars is coma. Coma is much more challenging to fix. Instead of a simple elongation, the star spreads out in a fan-like manner and fades. You can improve the appearance of comatic stars, but you often cannot fix them up as much as you would like.

The trick to fixing other types of elongation programs is to stretch a copy of the stars layer (or portions of it; see chapter *5, Selecting Stars*) in creative ways. In this example, you'll learn how to stretch a layer to correct elongation in the corners. The file for this exercise is:

\C8\Bubble_test.fit

After you apply basic Levels/Curves processing, use the Rectangular Marquee selection tool to select one corner of the image. Select only the portion of the corner that has elongated stars. Copy the selection to the clipboard, then paste it back into the image at

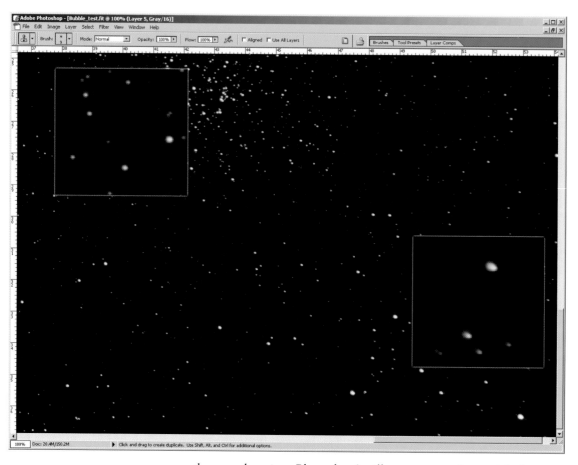

the same location. Photoshop® will create a new layer with the contents of the selection in it.

The image above shows enlargements of problem areas in the image. You are looking at the bottom right quadrant.

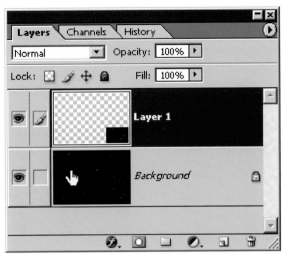

The enlargements show the extent of comatic error at the upper left and lower right of the selection. The Layers palette at left shows the actual size of the problem area in Layer 1.

Use the *Edit » Transform » Scale* menu item to activate the stretch mode. There are grab handles at the corners and in the middle of the edges. Use the middle-edge handles when you want to stretch in only one direction.

This particular image has elongation that is somewhat larger in the horizontal direction. (The stars at lower right are severely elongated because the STL-11000 camera's chip was too large for the refractor's flat field.)

❦ Tip: Make sure that the selection extends from the corner of the image and encloses only problem stars. You don't want to select any area where the stars are round; you want to stop at the point where the elongation ends.

If you were to simply offset the copied image, the results would not be useful. The stars at upper left would be over-corrected, and the stars at bottom right would be under-corrected. The stars in different portions of the image require different amounts of correction.

The method to use for correction remains the same: set the Blend mode of the layer on top to Darken.

The trick to getting different results in different parts of the image is to keep the top left of the copy layer (Layer 1) anchored, and to stretch (scale) the image from the lower right corner only.

❦ Tip: The elongation is radial, so the exact direction of the elongation varies by a small amount for different stars. You can use smaller sections of the image in multiple layers to help you get a more precise direction for each correction.

To correct this example of elongation, use the grab handles at middle-right and middle-bottom. You might need to zoom in or out, or move the image by holding down the spacebar and dragging with the mouse, in order to find these edge grab handles.

Carefully click the right-edge handle and drag it to the left. Watch the stars in the image to help you judge the best position. If you have trouble positioning the handle precisely, you can zoom in on the image by holding down the Ctrl key and clicking the plus ("+") key. Now move the bottom grab handle in the same manner. Adjust the right and bottom grab handles until the stars at lower right are round.

Note how this technique provides the greatest correction at bottom right, and progressively less correction as you move up and to the left. This corresponds to the difference in elongation between the two areas. This trick can work with all kinds of radial elongation.

✿ Tip: If some of the stars are over- or under-corrected, you can start with a smaller selection and use multiple passes. Pie-shaped slices are an especially effective way to divide up the area for processing, with each slice copied and pasted in as a layer. The rectangular selection used here is just an example; the quality of the results depends on both your eye and your work ethic!

Emission–Line Imaging: Acquisition

Emission-Line Imaging: Acquisition

Objective

Learn how to acquire images using emission-line (narrowband) filters.

Details

- What are emission-line filters, and why would I want to use them?
- Correct selection of emission-line filters
- Choosing the best camera for emission-line imaging
- How to use emission-line filters

Description

In the next three chapters, you'll explore the exciting world of emission-line photography of deep-sky objects. An emission line is a specific wavelength of light emitted by a specific energy level transition in a specific element.

One of the most common emission lines in the universe is the light emitted by a hydrogen atom when it "relaxes" (transitions) after being excited by the high-energy output of a hot, young star. H-alpha, as this emission is called, is at the wavelength of 656.3 nanometers (deep in the red end of the visible spectrum). An H-alpha filter isolates this wavelength, blocking all others.

Hydrogen and other elements have multiple emission lines associated with them; each represents a specific change of an electron from one orbit to another. Some transitions are more common than others, and it is these common transitions that make up the best opportunities for imaging by this "elemental light."

The techniques you will use for this type of imaging are similar in many ways to standard color imaging. But you will find that emission-line imaging places more demands on you, your equipment, and your processing skills.

NOTE: A great deal of scientific research and thought lies behind the electron transitions that power emission lines. A friend (and long-time advanced chemist) Steve Pastor has graciously written up an extensive discussion of the science that lies behind the wonderful field of emission-line imaging. The full text is included on the DVD:

\bonus\atomic_emission_lines-pastor.pdf

Definitions

Wavelength: All light is composed of waves. The distance between successive peaks in a wave is its wavelength. With sound, wavelength determines pitch. With visible light, wavelength determines color. The longest wavelengths we can see appear red, while the shortest appear blue or violet.

Nanometer (nm): For visible light, wavelengths are measured in nanometers, or billionths of a meter. Humans can see light with a wavelength from about 400nm (violet) to 700nm (red).

Interference filter: A type of filter that uses the wave nature of light to either block or pass light of specific wavelengths. Light that is desired to pass through the filter is made to constructively interfere, or add up. Unwanted wavelengths are made to destructively interfere, or subtract out.

Emission line: A certain, very specific wavelength emitted by an energized cloud of gas. Each chemical element, when excited by ultraviolet radiation, heated by collisions with other gas molecules, etc., will emit light at very specific wavelengths. By using appropriate filters, we can distinguish between different elements in an astronomical object.

NOTE: There are additional definitions throughout the chapter. They are located next to illustrations and discussions that provide additional context and make the definitions easier to understand.

Elements and Wavelengths

Narrowband emission-line imaging adds an exciting dimension to CCD astrophotography. Emission nebulae shine by the light of individual atoms radiating light of very specific colors (wavelengths). Consider the fate of an individual hydrogen atom as an example. When a hydrogen atom is struck by an energetic (ultraviolet) photon from a nearby hot star, it absorbs the photon. The atom's single electron jumps to a higher energy level as a result. This is an unstable configuration, and the electron eventually drops back down to an intermediate energy level, giving off a photon in the process. The photon contains exactly the energy difference between the two levels. This energy corresponds **exactly** to a specific wavelength of light: 656.3 nm (nanometers). This is just inside the visible spectrum, yielding a deep red color to the human eye.

This wavelength is called the hydrogen-alpha emission line. It is typically referred to simply as H-alpha. It is only one of the ways in which hydrogen can emit a photon. Other electron transitions result in different wavelengths of light. Other elements also have numerous transitions that result in specific wavelengths of light being emitted.

The physical matter in the universe is mostly hydrogen. The energy transition that produces the H-alpha emission line is the easiest transition that hydrogen makes. As a result, H-alpha is the most common source of emission in the universe. By using a special filter (called an emission-line or narrowband filter) to isolate this particular color, H-alpha light comes through the filter and all of the other wavelengths of light are almost completely blocked. This eliminates most of the star light, letting the nebula shine through. The result is an image which emphasizes detail that would otherwise be washed out by all of the other wavelengths of light present.

These narrowband filters can be made to isolate just about any specific wavelength of light. They eliminate virtually all light except the wavelength of interest. Not only do they block starlight, but they also block most light pollution. This is a significant added benefit of this type of imaging. You can take deep images from badly light-polluted locations, whether the pollution is man-made or natural (e.g., moonlight). The most effective filter for this type of imaging is H-alpha. Many other narrowband filters, such as Oxygen[III], occupy the same wavelength as common forms of light pollution.

❧ Tip: If you are using a refractor or camera lens, another advantage of emission-line imaging is that it is often possible to use inexpensive optics to obtain good images. Cheap optics typically suffer badly from chromatic aberration, where widely separated wavelengths of light come to focus at different places. Since only a very small range of wavelengths is being captured in emission-line imaging, chromatic aberration is not an issue.

There are three different types of emission-line imaging in common use:

Single-line (monochromatic) images: Images taken using a single emission-line filter. The most commonly used is hydrogen-alpha, but other filter types also can produce excellent images. The result is a black and white image.

Multiple-line "mapped color" images: Images taken with multiple emission-line filters and then combined into a color image. The data from different filters are assigned (mapped) to specific colors. The image of M42 at the start of this chapter is an example of this type of image.

Enhanced natural-color images: Images that combine narrowband images with conventional red/green/blue images. This is especially useful for taking deep images of nebulae from light-polluted locations.

Whatever type of imaging you do with emission-line filters, and whatever filters you use, there is one thing that remains the same: an emission-line filter will provide superior contrast. When imaging with a wideband filter, light of many wavelengths is recorded at the same time. A feature that might have good contrast in one wavelength might have poor contrast in other wavelengths. For example, an area that is dark in H-alpha could be bright in Oxygen[III]. The combination of light at various wavelengths effectively hides details in specific wavelengths. By isolating a single wavelength, you increase contrast and reveal details otherwise obscured.

Choosing Emission-Line Filters

Emission-line filters can be quite expensive, so it is important to know what you are buying. There are some key characteristics to bear in mind when choosing emission-line filters.

Passband: The range of wavelengths that are passed through the filter. For example, a hydrogen-alpha filter might pass any light with a wavelength from 653 to 659nm (nanometers).

As shown in the figure below, the passband has a tapered edge (bottom of curve). The filter manufacturer will typically specify the edge of the passband in terms of how much non-desirable light is rejected (e.g., 0.001% rejection out of band).

Bandwidth: The width of the passband in nanometers. A typical wideband red filter for regular color imaging might have a bandwidth of around 50nm. A narrowband H-alpha filter might have a bandwidth of only 3–10nm.

Transmission %: The amount of light that passes through the filter at the target wavelength. The figure below shows a typical transmission curve for an Astrodon H-alpha filter. It has a peak transmission of 91% right at the H-alpha line.

There are some trade-offs to make in choosing the bandwidth of filter to use. Ideally, an emission-line filter would let through one and only one wavelength of light, and thus have an infinitesimal bandwidth. But for practical reasons (and basic physical law), a finite bandwidth must be chosen.

A narrower filter bandwidth will remove more extraneous light. This increases the contrast of the nebular object in several ways:

- Most of the light from stars is blocked (only light in the passband of the filter passes through). This makes stars less obtrusive (many will not even show up in the image), allowing the nebula to be seen much more clearly.

  - Light pollution outside the passband is blocked.

  - Light from other emission lines is also blocked. From this it might seem that one should always choose the narrowest filter possible, but there are some important practical reasons why you might want to choose a filter with a larger bandwidth. It is important to distinguish between passband and bandwidth very carefully in order to understand the reasons behind this advice.

The passband of an interference filter is sensitive to the angle of the incoming light. As light enters more obliquely to the filter surface, the passband will shift towards shorter wavelengths. This is important because telescopes with faster focal ratios cause light to converge to focus at more oblique angles. For example, a telescope with a focal ratio of f/5 will have a much more oblique angle of incidence than a telescope with a focal ratio of f/10. Depending on the focal ratio of your telescope, there is a limit to how narrow the bandwidth of the filter can be. The faster the focal ratio, the more the passband will be shifted. At a sufficiently fast focal ratio, the passband can shift so much that the desired wavelength could be blocked!

The amount of shift is not a problem with most telescopes. However, when using fast camera lenses for astrophotography, passband shift can become important. The table below shows the minimum filter bandwidths that should be used with various focal ratios.

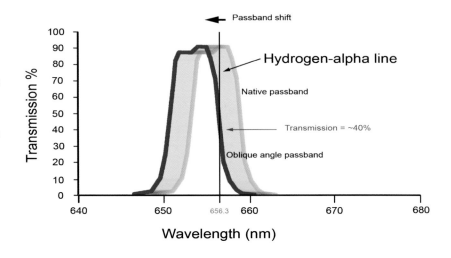

Focal Ratio	Minimum Bandwidth
f/5	1nm
f/3.3	2nm
f/2.5	4nm
f/1.8	6nm

⁂ Tɪᴘ: The passband always shifts to shorter wavelengths as the angle becomes more oblique. Look for narrowband filters designed with the wavelength of interest located at the shorter wavelength side of the passband. This gives more room for shifting with minimum consequences. The above table takes this design feature into account. The figure at upper right shows a passband shift due to an oblique angle of incidence.

Note that the transmission percentage due to the shift is only 40% of the H-alpha line.

⁂ Tɪᴘ: If your camera has a built-in guide chip, light reaching the guide chip also passes through the narrowband filter. This greatly reduces light throughout, and will make guiding more difficult. A wider bandwidth will pass more star light, and make guiding easier (at the cost of some contrast loss in your image). This trade-off is covered in more detail in the section on image acquisition.

Temperature shift: Changes in temperature can cause the passband of a filter to shift. Typical values of temperature shift are on the order of 0.02nm/°C. A filter with a wider passband will be less likely to block the desired wavelength in the presence of temperature shift. Note that this temperature shift is small enough that it is usually not an issue for deep-sky photography, which tends to use fairly wide filters. Solar H-alpha filters, on the other hand, typically have very narrow bandwidths on the order of 0.5nm and thus can be more sensitive to temperature shift.

Anti-reflective (AR) coatings: Most narrowband filters can be ordered with or without AR coatings. Coatings increase the price of the filter, but they significantly reduce reflections. These reflections usually show themselves as halos around bright stars; they are out-of-focus images of the same stars (due to reflections creating longer paths to the CCD chip).

Efficiency: Efficiency refers to how well a filter passes light within its passband. This term is often used incorrectly to indicate how much total light is allowed through; thus a wider filter might be wrongly called more "efficient" than a narrower one, when it should really be called "wider." Good interference filters can have passband efficiencies exceeding 90%. It is the transmission percentage at the wavelength of interest that is the key factor.

Leaks: Some inexpensive or poorly-designed filters will have many of the desired characteristics, but will "leak" light at undesired wavelengths. The most common example is a filter that lets through a lot of light in the near-infrared band. The extra light outside the desired wavelength reduces contrast in the image. The wider admitted bandwidth will also create focusing problems.

Filters made for visual use often leak profusely in the near-IR and/or UV bands. Since our eyes are not sensitive to this light, this is perfectly acceptable for a visual filter. Most CCD chips are sensitive to wavelengths well outside the visible range, and are often sensitive to near-IR wavelengths.

If using a leaky filter, be sure to also use a UV and/or IR blocking filter in tandem with it to eliminate the leaks in these bands. Also keep an eye out for another type of "leak:" filters that are not coated to the edge. Such filters can pass completely unfiltered light through gaps near the edge. Such problems can make a filter useless for CCD imaging.

Surface accuracy: Filters are made of one or more glass substrates, and imperfections in the polishing of these will result in wave-front errors in the final image. These errors are every bit as important, and are specified the same way as the optics in your telescope (peak to valley or RMS error). Also check out surface roughness specifications; a rough surface will scatter light and reduce contrast.

Parfocality: Filters are parfocal if you don't have to re-focus the optical system when changing from one to the other. While this can be convenient, many telescopes should be periodically re-focused due to changes in focus with temperature. Also, parfocality is harder to achieve with fast optical systems, since the critical focus zone is narrower.

Emission lines: Which emission lines should one target? H-alpha is a must, as it is the most common and brightest source of light from emission nebulae. Oxygen[III], responsible for the distinct teal color in many planetary nebulae, is a highly recommended choice. Other selections might include Sulfur-II and H-beta filters. The table on the next page shows the wavelengths of some common (and a few not so common) astronomical narrowband filters. Note that some emission lines have a secondary wavelength. These are cases where the emission isn't a simple electron orbital transition. Atoms with multiple orbitals can emit photons from other types of phenomena, such as an electron changing to a different orientation within the same orbital in order to align itself with the local magnetic field.

Filter Name	Wavelength of Interest
H-alpha	656
SulfurII	673
NitrogenII	658 (655)
Oxygen[I]	630
HeliumI	588
Oxygen[III]	501 (496)
H-beta	486
HeliumII	496
H-gamma	434
H-delta	410
Oxygen[II]	373
NeonIII	387

Filter suppliers: While this is not meant to be an exhaustive list, here are some suppliers of emission-line filters for amateur astrophotography: Custom Scientific, Schuler, Astronomik, Astrodon, and Santa Barbara Instruments Group. The figure at right shows the passbands and transmission percentage of filters from some of these suppliers.

Camera Considerations

Almost any camera that is used for long-exposure astrophotography can be used for emission-line imaging as well, but there are a few factors to consider that might make a particular model more or less suitable to emission-line imaging:

Quantum efficiency (QE): The more sensitive the camera (especially at the common emission-line wavelengths), the better it will be at detecting enough signal to overcome the camera's read noise. Higher QE results in cleaner images and allows shorter exposure times, if needed. You can find QE graphs that will give you the exact QE of a given CCD sensor at a given wavelength on the manufacturer's web site.

Anti-blooming (ABG): Anti-blooming cameras will do acceptable emission-line imaging, but they have lower QE overall than the non-antiblooming cameras, and thus longer

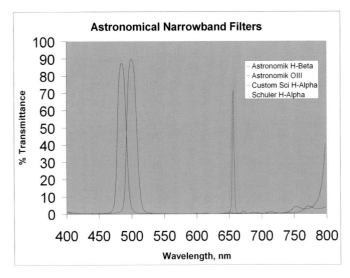

exposure times are required. In addition, light from stars is greatly attenuated by the emission-line filter and the stars are much less likely to bloom.

NOTE: Many ABG cameras have even lower QE at the H-alpha wavelength. Be sure to check the QE curve for any ABG cameras you plan to use for emission-line imaging carefully.

Noise and cooling: As will be covered in more detail later, noise in emission-line images is usually dominated by the dark-current and/or read noise of the camera. For this reason, cameras with low read noise will produce better results, as will cameras that can cool the sensor to colder temperatures, thereby reducing dark current.

Monochrome or color sensor: Many cameras are becoming available as "one-shot color" models. Instead of using a filter wheel and separate filters to generate color images, each individual pixel on the chip has a tiny dye-based filter over it. This is convenient for general-purpose color imaging, but has drawbacks for emission-line imaging:

- Dye-based filters are almost never as efficient as interference filters.
- There is a significant loss of resolution for emission-line imaging. The wavelength of interest will not reach many of the pixels on the chip. For example, when imaging with an H-alpha filter, the green and blue filters completely block the H-alpha wave-length. Light only reaches one out of every four pixels.
- Some emission lines, for example Oxygen[III], might fall partway between the passbands of the green and blue dye filters. This can sometimes result in poor transmission by both filters.

If you are using a one-shot color camera for emission-line imaging, strongly consider using its 2x2 binning mode, assuming the camera has that bin mode. This will help overcome camera read noise, but the result will still be significantly inferior to what you can achieve with monochrome cameras. The image below was taken with a monochrome camera.

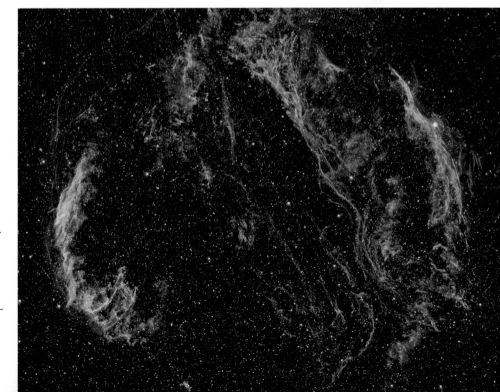

Equipment Issues

Emission-line photography is more difficult than regular wideband imaging: the individual exposures must be much longer. Emission-line filters let through very little light. Long exposures are needed to accumulate enough useful signal. Otherwise, signal from the object will be swamped by the camera's read and dark-current noise. Exposures of 2 to 10 minutes work with wideband filters, but exposures of 10 to 30 minutes are best for emission-line filters. For very narrow passbands or objects that emit small amounts of light, even longer exposures are needed.

Long exposures lead to a number of equipment issues that you will need to be aware of. These include polar alignment, optical quality, self-guiding, mount tracking, and use of external guide scopes.

Polar alignment: Because individual emission-line exposures are so long, polar alignment is critical. Poor polar alignment causes field rotation. The short exposures typical of wideband imaging seldom show this effect. Aligning images when you combine them removes any rotation effects. With the long exposures typical of emission-line exposures, field rotation might cause elongation of star images and smearing of nebula details in a single exposure. This effect is impossible to remove in processing, so you will want to spend more time perfecting your polar alignment for emission-line imaging.

Optical quality: You probably expect that better optical quality is always the best option. An interesting exception with emission-line work is that the color correction of a refractor is basically a non-issue. Only a tiny segment of the visible spectrum is captured when imaging through an emission-line filter, so chromatic aberration is a complete non-issue. Inexpensive doublet (achromat) refractors can produce good to very good results.

❧ Tip: You will typically need to refocus for different filters when imaging with an achromat because colors are not brought to the same focus. Also, the surface accuracy and collimation of the lens elements is still just as important as it is with wideband imaging—optical quality still determines how sharp your images will be.

Self-guiding: If your camera is a self-guiding model, the light that reaches the guide chip will also pass through the emission-line filter. This can dim (or even eliminate) the light from the guide star, making it much more difficult to find a suitable guide star. If your mount is a good performer, you can try extremely long guide exposures to compensate.

Mount tracking: Long exposures place very high demands on the tracking smoothness of the telescope mount. If your mount shows tracking errors that are faster than can be guided out, the first thing that can be tried is to train and enable the mount's periodic error correction (PEC) system, if it has one. Be sure to train it properly (i.e., over multiple revolutions of the worm gear, etc.). Products like PEMPro from CCDWare can help you get the most out of your mount's periodic error correction features.

Other guiding options: If you can't get good guiding even with PEC enabled, there are two options left. One is to use an external guide scope or off-axis guider, which allows you to guide with light that does not pass through any filters. This makes guiding much easier due to the shorter guide exposures, but it also introduces a new set of potential problems. The most important problem with external guide scopes is differential flexure between the main and guide scopes. This can cause star elongation in the image even though guiding might be very accurate. It is the guide scope that is being used as a reference, and if it moves relative to the imaging scope, star elongation will occur no matter how accurate the guiding.

If all else fails, you can upgrade to a better mount. It is very difficult to overcome the limitations of marginal equipment, but this is most true for emission-line imaging.

A stop-gap option might be to use optics with a shorter focal length. Mount errors that ruin photographs at two meters of focal length can be imperceptible at 500mm. Consider piggybacking a small refractor or camera lens on your main scope. (Be sure to keep the mount balanced when doing this.) The image below of the Rosette Nebula shows what you can accomplish when you have all aspects of emission-line imaging working well.

Acquisition Tips

Just as emission-line imaging places heavy demands on your mount, it also places new and more stringent demands on your image acquisition skills. Common skills like focusing become more critical, and new skills like dithered guiding will help you get better results.

Focusing: Focusing a telescope with an emission-line filter in the path can be more difficult than what you are used to. Unless there happens to be a bright star near the center of the field, you might need to slew to one nearby to focus, and then return to the object of interest. Focusing through a parfocal wideband filter can help with this, but make sure to do some testing to determine if your filters are truly parfocal. The faster your telescope's focal ratio, the more important this is.

Exposure length: In wideband imaging, it is often easy to take fairly short exposures and still overcome read noise, especially in light-polluted locations. But in emission-line imaging, even under a bright sky, it can be almost impossible to achieve this. The narrower the filter bandwidth, and the lower the QE of the camera, the more difficult this is.

The solution is to use individual exposures that are as long as you can reasonably achieve. You will be limited mostly by the performance limits of your mount and your guiding arrangement. If your equipment is capable, don't shy away from taking up to 30–minute or even longer individual exposures.

With some exceptionally bright nebulae, you can get away with shorter exposures. Indeed, some structures such as the trapezium area in M42 will require short exposures to avoid saturating the sensor, even with emission-line filters. This creates a bit of a dilemma: how to capture good data in the faint areas of such a nebula while not saturating or blooming the bright areas. A workable approach is to take two sets of exposures. Using M42 as an example, one might take a first set of exposures of one minute each to capture the trapezium area without saturation. A second set of ten-minute (or longer) exposures might then be taken to capture the faint outer structure of the nebula. The two (or more) sets of data could then be combined during processing in Photoshop® using layering and/or masking techniques.

Binning: The pixel binning option available in most cameras can be quite useful for emission-line imaging. This boosts the signal with respect to the read noise, and can make the difference between barely detecting the signal and not detecting anything at all.

Keep in mind that there is a sacrifice in resolution with binning. When doing multiple-line color images, it might be wise to shoot the H-alpha exposures un-binned, saving binning for exposures through the other filters. The H-alpha data would then be used as the luminance information, where the greatest detail is needed.

Total exposure time: The "think hours, not minutes" maxim applies doubly to emission-line images. In fact it might even be better to say, "think days, not hours." To get great data from a nebula, it might be necessary to spend multiple nights taking exposures of a single object.

Dithered guiding: Dithered guiding is beneficial for wide-band images, but it is vital for emission-line images. The signal in faint areas of emission-line images is almost always dominated by read and dark-current noise. Dithered guiding not only reduces the effect of dark-current noise, but also helps eliminate the effects of hot and cold pixels and any "pattern noise" in the individual exposures.

Dark frames: Emission-line images tend to be stretched much more aggressively in processing than their wideband counterparts. Because of this, and also because of the dominance of read and dark-current noise, small errors in dark frames can lead to obvious artifacts in the final image. Low-noise darks are essential, and the only way to get there is to take a large number of dark frames and to use statistical forms of combination, such as sigma-rejection. Eight to ten darks should be considered the absolute minimum; there is no upper limit.

Flats: Flat-field images are taken in the normal manner, but with longer exposure times. One thing to keep in mind is that some light sources, fluorescent lights in particular, emit almost no light at common emission-line wavelengths (e.g., H-alpha). The best choice is often to take sky flats, which are particularly easy to take with narrowband filters. Often, even a bright morning sky can be used, since so little light actually makes it to the CCD.

The image at right shows the Eagle and Swan Nebulae in Mapped Color. In this image, narrowband filters were used to isolate the light emitted by sulphur, hydrogen and oxygen atoms, which are energized by the bright young stars within the nebulae.

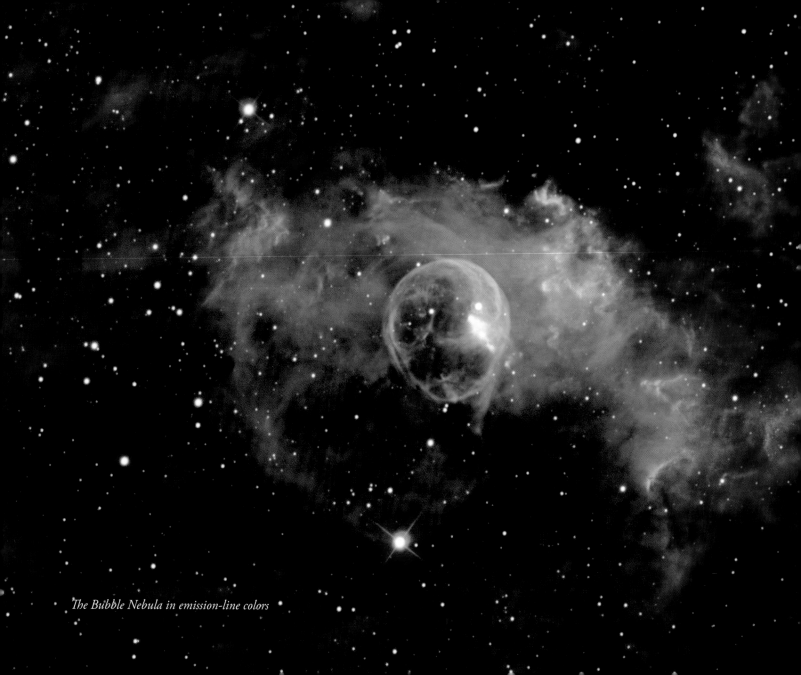

The Bubble Nebula in emission-line colors

Emission-Line Imaging: Processing

Emission-Line Imaging: Processing

Objective

Learn to control tonal range and color balance when processing a multi-band emission-line image.

Techniques
- Finding and equalizing background levels (MaxIm DL)
- Choosing color ratios and scaling the color channels (MaxIm DL)
- Working with DDP stretching and exporting (MaxIm DL)
- Saving image data in appropriate formats

Description

This chapter describes one possible workflow for processing an image that includes data from multiple emission-line filters. It also includes a discussion of the concepts behind the various steps, which will allow you to integrate your own ideas and methods into a workflow that meets your specific requirements.

The basic elements of this workflow include:

- Taking noise considerations into account
- Using the right internal data format (floating point)
- Image alignment
- Dealing with background levels
- Balancing emission-line color (more relaxed than for RGB/LRGB processing)

In addition, there are data files on the DVD that you will use in the tutorial section of this chapter to do you own color emission-line image processing.

Definitions

DDP: Stands for Digital Development Processing. This is an automated processing technique that makes a CCD image look more like a film image. CCD chips, unlike film, can record an enormous dynamic range in a linear fashion. Film, in contrast, has a much smaller dynamic range and by its physical nature compresses the dim and bright portions of that dynamic range. This compression allows us to see the entire dynamic range, which would otherwise be larger than the eye can see. DDP applies similar compression at the extremes to bring the image data within the range of brightness values that we can see.

Dynamic range: The number of steps that a CCD camera can distinguish. A camera that can output 65,536 different brightness levels doesn't often distinguish that many brightness levels. The read noise of the camera limits the number of brightness levels because the noise level defines the size of an individual step in the dynamic range. (You can't expect a camera to distinguish a brightness difference that is smaller than the amount of read noise!) The dynamic range is approximately equal to the full well depth divided by the read noise; consult your camera manual or the camera manufacturer's web site to obtain these numbers for your camera.

Floating-point format: A method of storing fractional numbers. Floating point is useful when saving combined or manipulated images. (Compare to Integer format, below.)

Integer format: The data from an image is a really long string of numbers. The most common method uses 16-bit integers to store the brightness level for each pixel. This allows for 65,536 brightness levels for each pixel. This is completely sufficient for individual exposures, since most of today's CCD cameras are unable to distinguish 65,536 different brightness levels (see Dynamic range). When images are combined, calibrated, or otherwise manipulated, fractional values can result. The integer format cannot store fractional values, resulting in a small loss of information. The solution is to use floating-point format to store manipulated images.

Quantization noise: Noise that is introduced into an image by quantizing, or rounding off, pixel values. For example, if one pixel has a value of 10.4, and another has a value of 10.6, these values would be rounded to 10 and 11, respectively, if the image is saved in an integer format. A similar (but even more dramatic) change happens when a 16-bit image is saved in 8-bit format. Quantization injects noise into the image that was not there previously and thus information is lost. The lost information cannot be recovered, so you will want to pay attention to all data conversions—even those that happen "behind the scenes" in the software without your direct knowledge. See integer format for a description of how this occurs during image manipulation.

Stretch: The process of altering the image's histogram. The need for stretching is based on the limitations of the eye compared to a CCD sensor. The eye has a very limited dynamic range. A histogram stretch typically expands the dim portions of the histogram and compresses the bright portions to allow us to see a reasonable visualization of the image data.

Prepare the Image

Before you can turn the emission-line data into an image, you need to pre-process the data:

- Image calibration (apply darks and flats)
- Create master images using data from each filter

There is very little difference in performing these steps on emission line and wideband data. However, you should keep one very important fact in mind: the signal level in emission-line images is usually much lower than in wideband images. Because of this, it is much easier to inadvertently introduce noise into an image by performing the wrong processing step at the wrong time. You'll want to pay closer attention to the details when working with emission-line images.

The fundamentals of good acquisition and processing remain important—even more important with emission-line images because you are working closer to the noise limits. These include the steps that help to control noise (uncertainty) in the final result:

- Long individual exposure times
- Long total exposure times
- Large numbers of calibration frames

Noise Considerations

CCD cameras output images in integer format, and most users always work in 16-bit integer format. However, when working with emission-line images, it is important to start

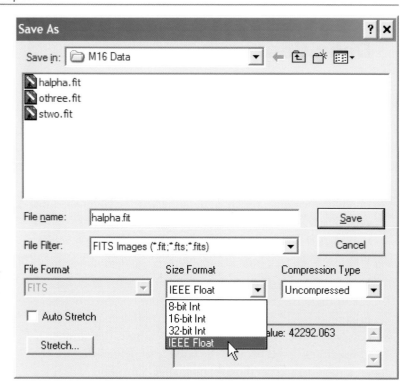

working with floating-point format. Floating point allows for higher precision than integer format does.

If the camera itself is working with integers, why use a higher-precision format? Consider what happens during imaging (acquisition *and* processing). As it happens, integer format only works well in the acquisition phase. Image processing can create numbers that will not fit into an integer file format.

For example, assume that a pixel is collecting photons and generating electrons at the rate of 10.5 per second. If the exposure length is one second, then one exposure might have

a count of 10 for this pixel, while another might have a count of 11 (since you can't have half of an electron). Over the course of many exposures, you would have roughly an equal number of exposures with 10 and 11 electrons.

During processing, when these exposures are averaged together, we would get the true value of 10.5. But if we use an integer format, the value of 10.5 can't be stored and the value gets rounded up to 11 (or down to 10, depending on the computer and software). If we use an integer file format, we will introduce small errors into the data.

Most (but not all) of the image processing software in use today supports floating-point format. The figure on the facing page shows how to select the IEEE Float format when saving a file in MaxIm DL. IEEE refers to the Institute of Electrical and Electronics Engineers, a standards-setting body. I recommend that you keep any data (other than raw images) in floating-point format, especially when you save to disk. This eliminates the risk of adding significant quantization noise to your images and allows you to realize the data's potential.

➤ TIP: The use of floating-point format applies to dark and flat exposures as well, not just object exposures. With emission-line images, it's very important to do everything you can to eliminate all sources of noise.

Processing the Image

This is where the real fun begins, and the process is very similar to regular LRGB color image processing. Once you have pre-processed the data, you have a single master image for each filter. The next step is to combine those images into an RGB image. This involves aligning (registering) the images so they line up with each other, selecting which image maps to which color channel, and then creating the RGB image.

➤ TIP: There are a number of good tools for image alignment (Registar, MaxIm DL, CCDSoft, etc.). If you use dithered guiding (and this is highly desirable because of how well it controls instrument artifacts), you have to align the individual images to make the master images. I suggest that you align all of the images to each other (from all filters) at one time if you have enough memory. Your master images will then be aligned when you are finished with pre-processing.

If you have mixed binning modes in your collection of master images, you will need to up-sample the lower resolution images. For example, if you have an unbinned (1x1) H-alpha image, and 2x2 binned SII and O[III] images, use the *Process »Double size* menu item in MaxIm DL (or the equivalent in other software) to up-sample the 2x2 binned images so they have the same resolution as the H-alpha image.

Equalizing the Background Levels

The next step is to equalize the background levels in the component images. Note the use of the word "background." In some images, especially at long focal lengths when imaging nebulae, you might not have any actual background in the image! Analyze the image to determine if you really have background present. Don't assume you have background just because the dimmest portion of the image is very dark. For example, when imaging the Swan nebula (Messier 17), it's easy to assume that the dark area near the nebula is back-

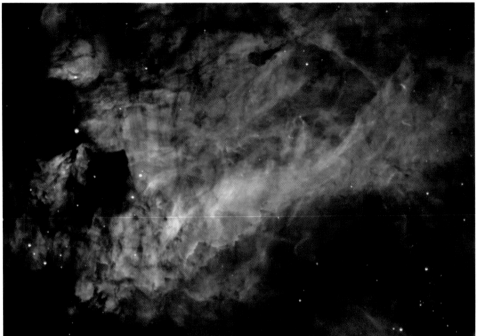

ground. As the figure at right shows, there is a lot of very dim nebulosity around M17. Even though the outer edges of the image look like background, there is faint nebulosity everywhere—the exposure wasn't long enough to show all of the nebulosity that is present.

There are two cases to deal with when working with emission-line images:

- The image has at least some true background. In this case, the level of the background can be regarded as black for processing of the image.
- The image has no background. In this case, you will want to use a brighter level for the darkest parts of the image. Since they are nebulosity, not true background, you can render them with a bit of brightness even if your exposure isn't deep enough to record any details.

If you can't figure out which case applies to your image, you can search online for deeper images that will give you the information you need to decide. In the end, however, it is up to your aesthetic sensibilities to determine what you want to do.

There are various ways to find the darkest area in the image, and to quantify the brightness level in that area. In MaxIm DL, use the Information window (see image on facing page). In Aperture mode, the Information window reports an average of the pixel values in the area under the cursor. You can

move the cursor around the image to compare areas that look like good candidates for a background level.

You can use the Information window's Area mode to permanently alter the background level. Draw a rectangle in the area you identified as the background. Take note of the brightness of this area (use the Average value in the Information window), and then use the "Pixel Math" command (under the *Process* menu) to subtract a value that will leave a 100-count background. This leaves a 100-count pedestal "below" the data as a safety factor. For example, if the background average is 180, enter a value of –80 in the Add Constant field of the Pixel Math window.

Balancing Emission-Line Color

This is the most interesting aspect of multiple-line imaging. With regular RGB/LRGB imaging, the goal is to achieve an accurate color balance—to reproduce what is out there accurately. With emission-line imaging, the goal is to use color balance to reveal interesting structure in the image. Put another way, the goal is to fully realize the potential of that hard-won data, revealing the different emission-line signal levels in the nebula.

One could take a purist approach and do a true color balance between the different channels, correcting for camera QE, atmospheric extinction, etc. That would yield an image dominated by the hydrogen-alpha channel. Hydrogen is the most abundant element in the universe, but other elements are also interesting. Holding back on the hydrogen to allow the contribution of other elements to show through typically yields the most interesting and informative results.

The structure revealed by emission-line imaging is based on energy. So it is not just the concentrations of the elements themselves that are interesting, but the

energy levels they reveal at various places in the nebula. The energy involved in emission-line imaging starts out as ionizing radiation (energetic photons) that raises some electrons to higher energy levels and kicks other electrons out of the atom. The process of settling back to a nominal energy level results in the emission of photons at specific energy levels (wavelengths). These are the photons we seek to capture.

The atoms that emit photons at longer wavelengths are more easily excited. A good example is H-alpha. The reason behind this is that longer-wavelength (red) photons have less energy than shorter-wavelength (blue) photons. A kick involving less energy occurs more easily, and thus more often. This means

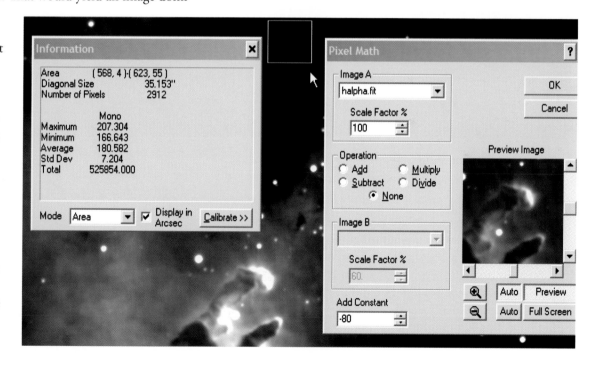

signal close to bright stars and along shock fronts. Further away, the lower energy (red) H-alpha signature remains strong because the exciting energy is still sufficient to energize the transition. In the dim outer reaches of a nebula, even H-alpha emission begins to fade. But sulfur, with a slightly longer wavelength than hydrogen, has low enough energy requirements that it can be excited to emit its low-energy light.

Choosing the Color Ratios

For this example we'll start with MaxIm DL's *Combine Color* function under the *Color* menu (see image at left).

that emission-line imaging won't reveal the presence of an element unless the element is receiving enough ionizing radiation to bump electrons up to the right energy levels.

For all we know, there might be oxygen distributed throughout a nebula, but the oxygen further away from the stars generating the exciting radiation (ultraviolet light) will be less easily ionized. The most often imaged Oxygen ion is O[III], which emits in the blue/green part of the spectrum. This is a relatively high-energy transition, so we find a strong oxygen

Use this dialog to explore the effect of different color weights (combine ratios). Load the following files into MaxIm DL:

If you would like to follow along with this exercise, open the following files from the DVD in Photoshop CS (or later):

\C10\halpha.fit
\C10\othree.fit
\C10\stwo.fit

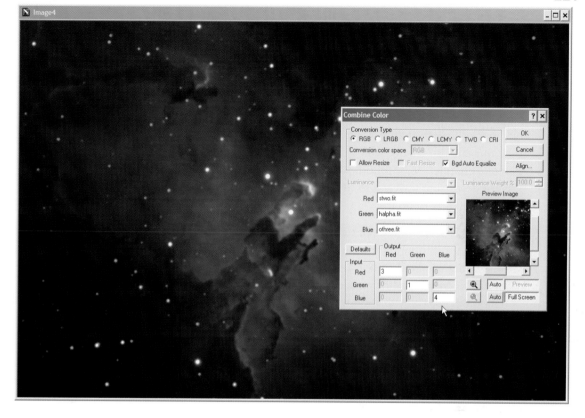

These are floating-point master images created from multiple individual frames. Use the drop down for the red channel to select the SII image. Select H-alpha for the green channel, and the O[III] image for the blue channel. This puts the images in strict energy order, with the longest wavelength data in red, and the shortest wavelength date in blue.

Make sure that the *Bgd Auto Equalize* check box is checked. This image has virtually no background, so we are using this tool here only to avoid introducing a color bias into the image as you play with the color ratios. Remember to turn it off before you commit the ratios.

☀ TIP: Manual background equalization is described on page 217. A tutorial from Ron's first book, *The New CCD Astronomy,* is included on the DVD at **\C10\bgd_eq.pdf**. Or load the already-equalized images, with "**_eq**" in the filenames.

In the preview window (see facing page), you can see that the color is mostly green. This is due to the preponderance of hy-

drogen in the nebula as described above. What we want to do now is to find a set of color ratios, represented by the matrix at the bottom of the dialog box, that yield a color image that yields the best use of the visible color spectrum.

☀ TIP: Zoom in and out in the preview window using the plus/minus icons. Hold down the control key and slide the cursor in the preview image to view other parts of the image.

Note that there is nothing particularly scientific about this approach to setting the color ratios. We are using color to represent real variations in the data, but the specific colors that we end up with will not necessarily represent the actual ratios of the elements present in the nebula.

If you'd rather view the entire image, use the Full Screen button. You can also change which image is associated with which color channel. Many photographers like to keep them in order of decreasing wavelength (increasing energy), but that is only one way to do it.

 Tip: The noise levels in each of the three master images are different. This limits how far you can push the color balance. The noisiest data will be the limiting factor in how far you can adjust color. Noisy data yields weak color. If you try to push noisy data too hard, you still wind up with weak color.

Once you have settled on satisfactory color ratios, write them down. Note that in the above example, the H-alpha channel setting was kept at 1. This just makes it easier for the next step, as that channel won't have to be modified.

Scaling the Color Channels

The *Bgd Auto Equalize* function in the Combine Color dialog box will often clip the data when there is widespread nebulosity. Use the *Process » Pixel Math* menu item instead (see dialog at upper right) to scale the SII and O[III] data.

Since we chose a scale factor of 3 for the SII data in the Color Combine dialog box, set the Scale Factor for that image to 300 (percent).

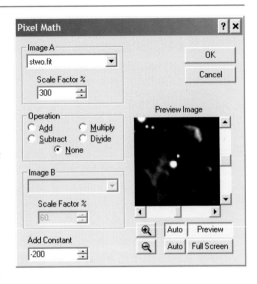

NOTE: This also will scale the 100-count pedestal that we left in the data, so 200 counts must also be subtracted from the scaled data to keep the pedestal at 100. For the O[III] data, scale by 400% and subtract 300 counts to maintain the pedestal at 100 counts. If you are going to color balance in Photoshop®, you can do bias correction there as well, but it will be less precise.

Combining the Data

At this point, you are ready to do the final color combine. Use the "Combine Color" function again, but reset the color ratios all to 1 since we have now scaled the data using Pixel Math. Be sure to uncheck the Bgd Auto Equalize check box.

 Tip: Since the H-alpha data has a very good signal-to-noise ratio, you can change to an LRGB combine at this point using H-alpha as both the green and luminance channels.

Click the OK button to create the color-combined image. I recommend saving not only this color combined version, but also the intermediate versions of the H-alpha, O[III], and SII images. Be sure to use floating-point format.

DDP stretching and exporting the image

Up to now the data has been kept in the floating point format. Final contrast adjustments will be done in Photoshop®, but it only works in integers. We now need to perform a heavy non-linear stretch on the data to make it safe to convert to integer format, and we want to prevent the injection of quantization noise into the image.

Raw astronomical images usually contain most of their interesting information at the dark end of the histogram, and the brightness levels of these details are usually jammed together. Put another way, the difference in brightness within interesting areas of the image is much smaller than the total brightness range of the image. This is especially true of most emission-line images.

Because we are going to stretch the Dim zone and compress the Bright zone, we care very much about even very small differences in the brightness. Even a difference between two pixels of less than one count is significant. For example, one pixel might have a value of 10.0, and another might have a value of 10.4.

Sometimes, the noise in the image will make a difference of a fraction of a pixel unimportant. But sometimes the noise is low enough that a small difference in pixel values is significant. We want to make sure we don't

throw away that information by introducing rounding errors into the data. One excellent way to avoid this is to first stretch the data before converting to integer format.

The stretching action of Digital Development Processing (DDP) is a very useful function for performing this stretch. It can also work well for doing most of the stretching you would want to do to your image.

The original definition of DDP (from Dr. Kunihiko Okano) includes unsharp masking (sharpening) in addition to strong nonlinear stretching. This sharpening can sometimes be problematic, leading to dark halos around stars. Fortunately the sharpening action can in effect be disabled in MaxIm DL (see image below).

Use the menu item *Filter » Digital Development...* In the resulting dialog, click the *Set User Filter...* button. This displays the User Filter dialog. Set the center box of the filter kernel to 1, and all other entries to 0. This disables the sharpening ac-

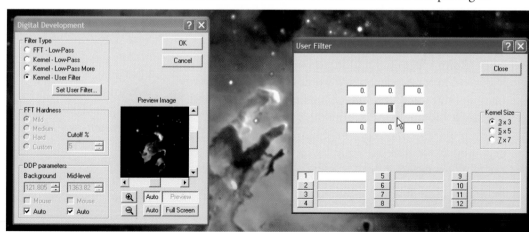

tion by defining a user filter that does nothing to the data. Click the Close button to save this change.

In the DDP Parameters section of the Digital Development dialog, select both Auto checkboxes to establish default Background and Mid-level settings. This gives good starting points, but it's important to tweak these settings to optimize your results. Uncheck the Auto settings so you can make manual adjustments to the defaults. Typically, lower the Background setting by 100 to avoid clipping, and raise the Mid-level setting by 20%.

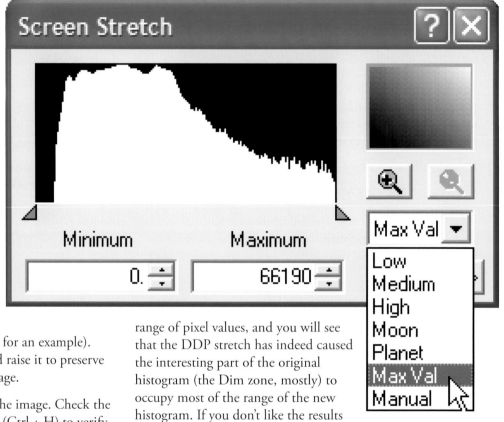

❧ Tip: Experiment with the Mid-level setting to get more or less "boost" from the algorithm (see the image on page 11 for an example). Lower the Mid-level for more boost, and raise it to preserve more detail in the bright parts of the image.

Click OK to apply the DDP stretch to the image. Check the histogram in the Screen Stretch window (Ctrl + H) to verify that the DDP stretch has not clipped the data on the black end of the histogram. Make sure there is at least a small gap between the left-hand edge of the histogram display and the beginning of the data (see figure at upper right). If not, redo the DDP operation with a lower Background value.

To see what the stretch actually did, select the "Max Val" setting in the screen stretch window. This will show the entire range of pixel values, and you will see that the DDP stretch has indeed caused the interesting part of the original histogram (the Dim zone, mostly) to occupy most of the range of the new histogram. If you don't like the results or want to adjust the Background and Mid-level settings, simply undo the change and re-apply with the new settings. Don't be overly concerned if the image looks a bit darker than you would like; this can easily be adjusted using Photoshop®. The main point is to get most of the stretching done and to make the data safe for conversion to integer format, all in one step.

Now that the DDP stretch has been performed, it is safe to save in an integer format. Make sure this is a 16-bit format by confirming that 16-bit Int is the Size Format setting (see image at lower right).

⁂ TIP: The default color file format for MaxIm DL is FITS. Unfortunately, there isn't any universal standard on what a color FITS file should look like. As a result, if you save in the default format, you might not be able to open your file in Photoshop® or other image processing programs.

Select the TIFF format in the File Format drop-down. If the File Format drop-down is not available (as shown here), use the File Filter drop-down to select TIFF Images. This is extremely important; saving in the wrong format makes the file unusable.

The techniques described in this chapter use simplified processing by using automated tools such as DDP. This is a good introduction to emission-line imaging with multiple filters, but automated tools only take you part of the way.

As your image processing skills advance, you can move on to more sophisticated processing by following these steps:

- Save an RGB-only TIFF file with the results of your combine.
- Open the RGB file in Photoshop®.
- Open the H-alpha data in Photoshop®.

- Do all of the processing on the H-alpha data in Photoshop®, using Zone System techniques.
- As with a conventional LRGB image, set up one layer for the "luminance" (H-alpha) data, and another for the "color" (emission-line combination) data. This allows you to apply the right processing to the right type of data.

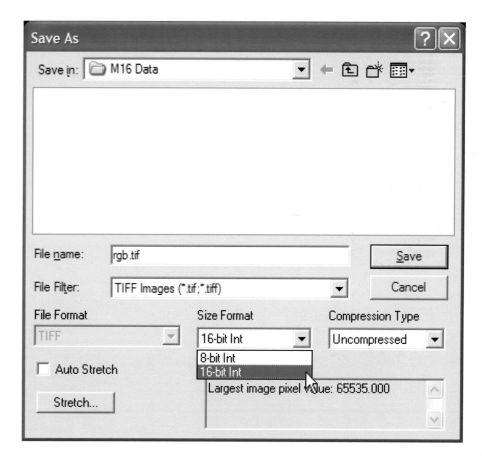

NGC 281 in emission-line colors

Emission-Line with Natural Color

Emission-Line with Natural Color

Objective

Enhance the color and depth of a regular RGB/LRGB image using emission-line data.

Techniques

- Luminance layering
- Image alignment with Free Transform

Description

This chapter describes how to enhance regular wideband images using emission-line data. You can apply emission-line data to both RGB and LRGB images.

You can enhance your images in two ways:

- Improve the depth (contrast) and color of the main subject of the image
- Overcome light pollution by adding emission-line data

These techniques are related, but it's useful to point out that you don't need to suffer from light pollution in order to make use of emission-line data in regular images. Adding emission-line data to a regular RGB image allows you to produce a natural-color image with depth that would otherwise be unattainable.

The workflow presented here is just one approach to integrating RGB/LRGB and emission-line data. Once you learn these steps and the concepts behind them, you can experiment with your own ideas.

Definitions

LRGB: An image composed of both luminance (L) and color (RGB—red, green, blue) data. Typically, the luminance layer sits below the color layer. (In Photoshop®, you can use Merge Channels to create an RGB image from separate red, green, and blue images.)

Luminance Layering: The practice of putting the luminance data in a layer above the color data. This is functionally equivalent to the Zone System, but not as flexible—if you have multiple luminance layers, you are better off to put color above luminance. The Zone System makes frequent use of multiple luminance layers, so use Luminance Layering only where it gives you a specific advantage.

Mosaic: A final image made up of multiple images which have been aligned and processed to fit together seamlessly. The key word here is seamless. There is a chapter on creating a mosaic in Ron Wodaski's first book, *The New CCD Astronomy*.

Opacity: The degree to which you can "see through" one image or layer to what lies behind/below it. This is commonly used in Photoshop® for blending images, and for aligning images. When blending, you need to set an opacity percentage for the top/front image/layer that provides the result you like. When reducing opacity for alignment, the change is only temporary and you will usually restore the original opacity after the alignment is complete.

Parfocal: When filters come to focus at the same focus position, they are said to be parfocal. Filters are seldom exactly parfocal, and the faster your optics the less likely the filters are to be truly parfocal. A telescope at f/5 or faster might well show a slight non-parfocal result, while slower telescopes (especially slower than about f/8) are much more likely to give parfocal results. The difference? The depth of focus (the critical focus zone) is smaller on faster telescopes, so that even small differences in focus position will lead to non-parfocal results. Depending on when and where you buy emission-line filters, they might or might not be parfocal with your regular color filters.

RGB: An image composed only of RGB (red, green, blue) data. Often combined with a luminance layer to create an LRGB image. In this chapter, you learn how to combine emission-line data with one or more specific channels in an RGB or LRGB image, which is not the same thing as an LRGB image. In an LRGB image, the RGB data provides all the color information. In an emission-line enhanced color image, the emission-line data is merged with a specific color channel to enhance the appearance and/or information in that channel.

Allowed/Forbidden Transitions: An energy-releasing electron transition that occurs very rarely (it is not truly forbidden). Transitions that involve a change in the number of unpaired electrons are forbidden; transitions that have a change in orbital angular momentum = ±1 are allowed. The subject is extremely complicated—too complicated by far for a mere definition. You'll find a reference to a white paper on this subject on the DVD; the reference to the paper can be found in the *Description* section of chapter 9. Forbidden transitions are shown enclosed in brackets. For example, the doubly-ionized Oxygen transition is forbidden, and is shown as O[III].

m27_lrgb_ddp.tif @ 66.7% (RGB/16#)

Two Approaches

There are two basic ways to add emission-line data to a wide-band RGB image:

- Use an emission-line image (e.g., Hydrogen-alpha), to augment the luminance channel of the RGB or LRGB image. This method uses standard Zone System techniques, including luminance layering.
- Enhance the RGB color information with the emission-line data. This involves techniques not normally used in wide-band imaging.

Luminance Enhancement

For this example we'll start by opening the following files in Photoshop® CS or later:

If you would like to follow along with this exercise, open the following files from the DVD in Photoshop® CS (or later):

\C11\M27_lrgb_ddp.tif
\C11\M27_halpha_ddp.tif

The first step is to process each of these images using the normal Zone System techniques. Apply any techniques you would normally use in Photoshop® or other programs: Levels, Curves, DDP (e.g., in MaxIm DL). The examples above and on facing page show how I processed these images. I stretched both images with DDP in MaxIm DL (without sharpening), followed by minor adjustments in Photoshop® using Levels and Curves.

🍃 Tip: For any color combine, but especially for emission-line enhancement, it's a good idea to hold back on your processing. Push each source image less than you would for stand-alone presentation. In particular, if the H-alpha image is made too bright, it will tend to wash out the colors in the combined image.

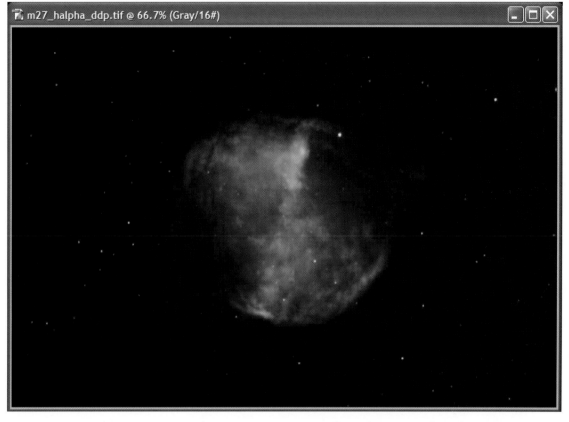

m27_halpha_ddp.tif @ 66.7% (Gray/16#)

One image is a Regular wide-band LRGB image of M27, taken under a light-polluted suburban sky. The other is an H-alpha image of M27.

Sometimes, before you can combine images, you will need to align (register) them. While this might seem obvious and trivial, alignment can sometimes be a problem for composite wideband/narrowband images. The reason lies in the effect of focus on image scale. Emission-line filters are often not parfocal with the LRGB filters, and the telescope must be re-focused between exposures. Refocusing can change the focal length of the telescope slightly, which in turn can make small changes to the magnification of the image. This makes registration of the resulting images more challenging.

There are two ways to perform alignment when the images are slightly different in size:

- Use a software program that specializes in this operation, such as RegiStar (www.aurigaimaging.com). Some camera control programs can handle resizing only with respect to binning, so check your software to see if it can handle this sort of task.

- Use the Free Transform Tool in Photoshop® to resize the smaller image to match the larger.

RegiStar is available from Auriga Imaging. It provides extremely accurate results, and is also quite useful for assembling mosaics. The interface takes some effort to master, but the accuracy of the program makes it well worth your while.

For this example, the source images are already registered. After any histogram adjustments, copy the H-alpha image onto the LRGB image. You can use the clipboard, but the simplest method is to right click on the "Background" layer in the Layer palette and use the *Duplicate Layer* selection on the popup menu. In the dialog that appears, you can enter a name for the new layer, and you can also select the document

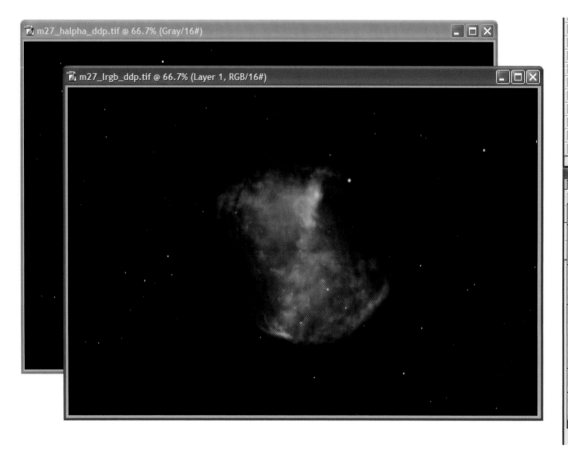

to copy the layer into. This is much harder to describe than it is to do! Duplicating a layer into another document, however, is a very powerful and useful technique.

Either way, the end result is a new layer in the LRGB image. Set the blending mode of the H-alpha layer to **Luminosity**, as shown in the figure on facing page.

By default, the H-alpha data is at 100% opacity, so it completely replaces the luminance from the LRGB image. The

result is an image that definitely emphasizes the nebula, but perhaps too much so. The strength of the H-alpha data causes the color in the nebula and stars to become weaker (a process called desaturation). This looks unnatural. You can obtain a more natural look by reducing the opacity level to somewhere in the 50–60% range. The figure below shows the appearance of the image at an opacity setting of 54%.

🐾 TIP: The combination of a base layer with a luminance layer above it is called Luminance Layering. You can apply

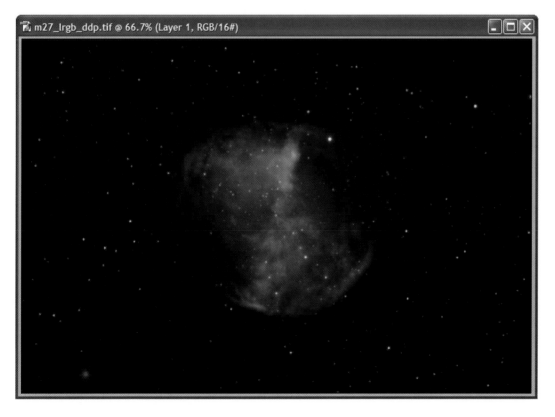

sharpening and other luminance-specific processing to the luminance layer according to your preferences. Color operations, such as color balance and saturation, can be performed on the underlying layer. Luminance Layering is functionally the same as the layering used in the Zone System, but the luminance is on top of the color and the blend mode of the upper layer is Luminance instead of Color. Since the Zone System allows the use of multiple luminance layers (e.g., one or more layers of stars), putting color on top is more often the best choice for standard LRGB images.

In this example, luminance information is derived from both layers because the opacity of the H-alpha layer is not 100%. If you want to perform luminance-specific operations on a luminance layer, you can:

1. Duplicate the LRGB layer (called Background).
2. Desaturate the copy using *Image»Adjustment»Desaturate.*
3. Combine the H-alpha layer (with its opacity set to 54%) and the desaturated copy into a single layer.
4. Set the blend mode of the new layer to Luminosity.

This completes luminance enhancement. At this point you can make final adjustments using Levels and Curves, and perform any other processing (clean up background color gradients, etc.).

Color Channel Enhancement

Using emission-line data for the luminance channel has both advantages and disadvantages. On the plus side, you can often get dramatic improvement in the contrast and detail in the image. The potential problem is that the emission-line data only represents a single wavelength (color). With luminance layering, the brightness of the emission-line data applies to all of the colors.

With color channel enhancement, you can control which color channel the emission-line data applies to. For this example, we'll enhance an LRGB image of M27 with H-alpha and [OIII] data. The H-alpha data matches the red channel. The [OIII] data fits right on the boundary of the blue and green channels, so you will apply it to both of those channels.

If you would like to follow along with this exercise, open the following files from the DVD in Photoshop® CS (or later):

\C11\M27_halpha_ddp.tif
\C11\M27_lrgb_ddp.tif
\C11\M27_othree_ddp.tif

NOTE: The practice data for this example has already been stretched using DDP and aligned in MaxIm DL, with sharpening disabled. It is ready to use. The figure on facing page shows the three files open in Photoshop®.

We'll use the H-alpha data to enhance the red channel of the LRGB image. Begin by duplicating the H-alpha image into

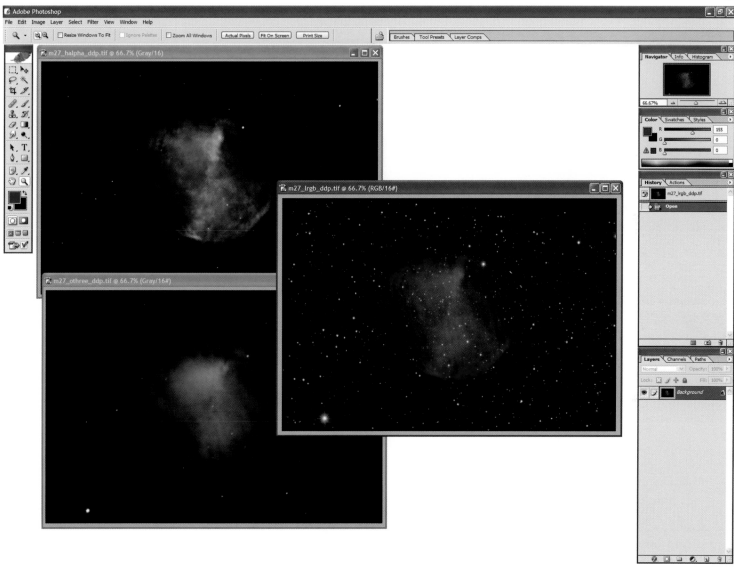

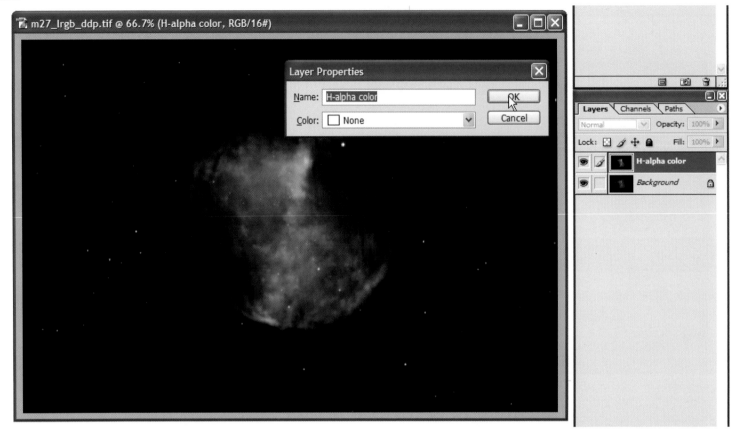

the LRGB image (*Layer » Duplicate Layer;* see result on page 238). The image now has two layers: the background color image, and the grayscale H-alpha image above it.

❧ TIP: Name your layers to help keep track of them. In this example, we'll have multiple layers and names to make them easier to keep track of. The figure above shows the H-alpha layer being named "H-alpha color" using the Layer Proper-

ties dialog (right click on a layer to access this dialog). You can name the layer during duplication, or afterwards if you duplicate using copy and paste.

The key trick is to make the H-alpha data affect only the red channel. One way to accomplish this is by clearing out all but the red channel in the H-alpha layer. See "H-alpha as red channel" on the facing page for step-by-step instructions.

1 Go to the Tools palette, and verify that the background color is set to black. If it is not black, click the tiny icon immediately below left of the tool icon, then click the reverse icon above right.

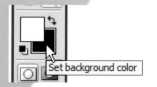

2 Go to the Layers palette, and select the H-alpha layer by clicking on its name. This ensures that only the H-alpha data will be affected by the operations that follow.

3 Switch to the Channels palette, and select both the green and blue channels (first select one by clicking on its name, then hold down shift and select the other).

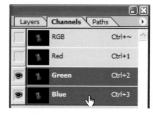

4 In the image, select all (Ctrl A), then press the Delete key. This will set the green and blue channels to black, leaving just the red channel containing the H-alpha data. Click on the checkbox next to the "RGB" channel in the Channels palette. Your screen should now looking something like the figure at bottom right.

H-alpha as red channel

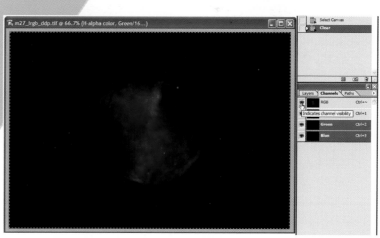

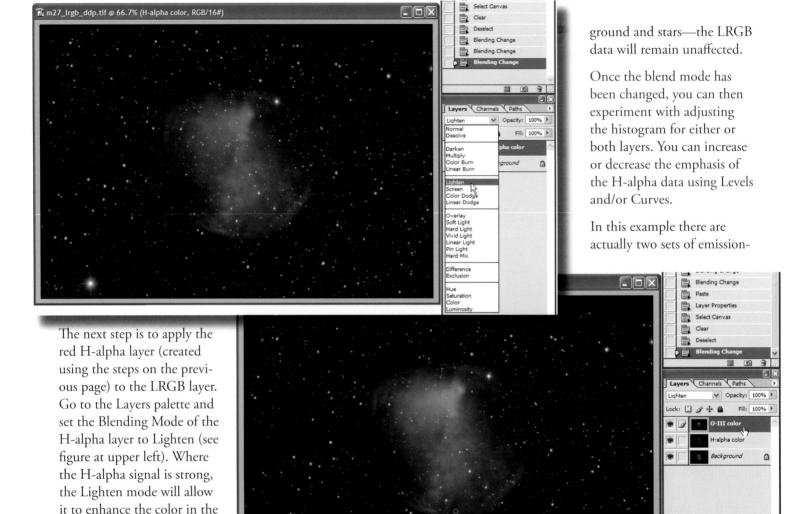

ground and stars—the LRGB data will remain unaffected.

Once the blend mode has been changed, you can then experiment with adjusting the histogram for either or both layers. You can increase or decrease the emphasis of the H-alpha data using Levels and/or Curves.

In this example there are actually two sets of emission-

The next step is to apply the red H-alpha layer (created using the steps on the previous page) to the LRGB layer. Go to the Layers palette and set the Blending Mode of the H-alpha layer to Lighten (see figure at upper left). Where the H-alpha signal is strong, the Lighten mode will allow it to enhance the color in the red channel of the LRGB image. Where the H-alpha signal is weak—in the back-line data, and I recommend adding the [OIII] data before adjusting the histogram. Add the [OIII] data to the image as another layer, using the same technique you used for the H-alpha data. Instead of deleting the green and blue channels, delete the red channel. This will allow the [OIII] data to take on its natural cyan color (partly green, partly blue). Set the Blend Mode of the [OIII] layer to Lighten as well. You should now see something like the example in the figure at bottom right on the facing page.

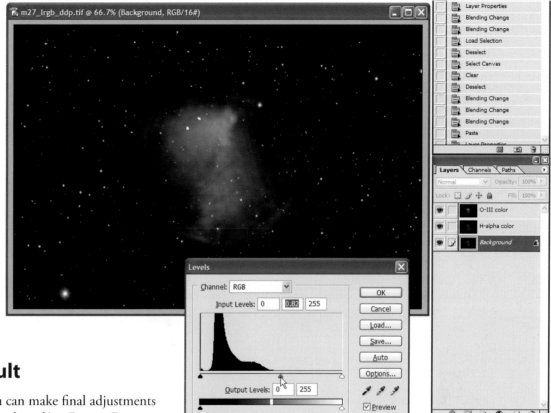

Processing the Result

Once the layers are in place, you can make final adjustments to each layer histogram using Levels and/or Curves. By decreasing the brightness of the LRGB layer, for example, the stars become dimmer and tighter. This happens because the narrowband images are contributing more to the final result. The H-alpha and [OIII] data will remain in the red and green/blue channels and the nebula will really begin to stand out. The figure above shows the result of a Gamma change in Levels, from 1.00 to 0.82, darkening the LRGB layer.

At this point, final adjustments are determined mainly by your imagination and sense of style. You are creating your interpretation of this object, so experiment and have fun. Decide what details you want to emphasize and how strongly or subtly you want to do so. The two methods covered here—luminance enhancement and color enhancement—can also be used in combination to add another degree of freedom. You might try pasting the grayscale H-alpha image on top as an additional layer, setting its blend mode to luminosity. By adjusting the opacity of this layer, we can add even more emphasis to the tufts of hydrogen gas distributed throughout the nebula (see figure below).

Think of the steps and techniques presented in these chapters on emission-line imaging as keys on a piano. These are the notes that can be used, if played with sufficient skill, to create a coherent melody. Learn where the keys are and how to strike them to get just the effect you want. You might even discover new keys along the way. Then have at it—let the pixels fly and create celestial symphonies of your own!

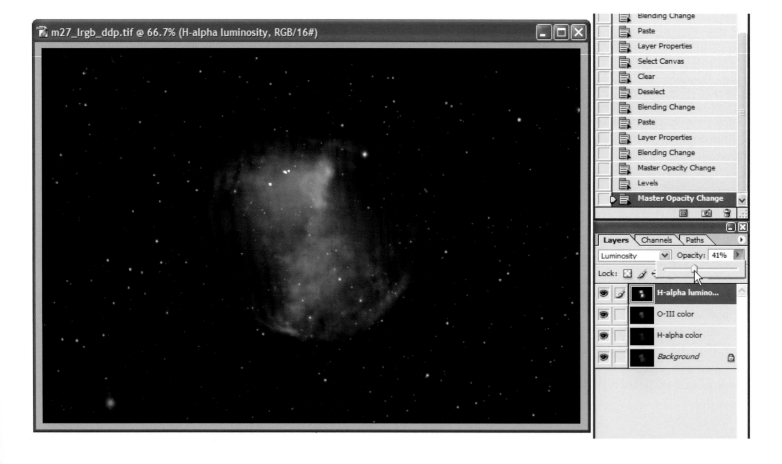

Free DVD and Web Content

The book references image files and other resources that are available to readers. See the information at right on obtaining your copy of the DVD and/or access to the web content.

The DVD/Web content includes:

⇨ A bonus chapter on image acquisition workflow. This is similar in scope to chapter 4, but it focuses on the stuff you can do to improve images before and while you take them.

⇨ Image processing training videos. Some of these are detailed videos of techniques described in the book, and some are on other topics, both advanced and beginning. Video training is provided by the author and others.

⇨ FITS files for the tutorials in the book.

⇨ Electronic version of the book. (DVD only)

⇨ Bonus software from New Astronomy Press Software (De-Bloomer, Gradient Remover)

How to Obtain Your Free DVD

You are entitled to a free DVD when you purchase this book. The DVD does not come with the book; it will be sent to you by mail. If you bought the book directly from the publisher, the DVD is sent out automatically. If you bought the book from a bookstore or astronomy store, you can request a copy of the DVD by sending us the information listed below.

⇨ Contact information. This includes your name, address, phone number, and email address. We will not give out the information to anyone; we use it to keep track of who has received the DVD, and to provide access to the book web site.

⇨ Place of purchase. This is the name of the bookstore or astronomy store (including online) where you bought the book.

⇨ A copy of your receipt or other proof of purchase. If you do not have proof of purchase, you can download the DVD materials from the book web site. You will still need to register as above in order to access the web site.

If you do have your receipt, you can scan it and email it to us at support@newastro2.com with the above information.

If you do not have your receipt, or you cannot scan it, you can cut out the proof of purchase below and mail it to us with the above information included.

Proof of purchase

The Zone System

Russell Croman Resources

Russell Croman has created various tools for astro imagers that are available for download from his web site. In addition, you can purchase printed copies of many of Russell's fine images from his web site:

http://www.rc-astro.com/resources

At the time the book was printed, the following resources were available:

Software

⇨ GradientXTerminator - A sophisticated gradient removal plug-in for Adobe Photoshop®. Even works on 16-bit and color images!

⇨ Cloud Sensor Graph - A program for graphing the output of the Boltwood Cloud Sensor.

⇨ RC-Astro Processing Console - This plug-in for MaxIm DL contains multiple image processing algorithms, including a new version of the SigmaReject Combine function.

⇨ SigmaReject - This plug-in for MaxIm DL combines multiple images, rejecting pixel values outside specified limits.

Articles

⇨ Astrophotography: Art or Science?

⇨ Position a focal reducer on a Ritchey-Chrétien Cassegrain Telescope

Talks

⇨ Preserving Star Colors - How to avoid loss of star color during image processing (originally presented at the 2004 Advanced Imaging Conference).

Other

⇨ LLRGB Processing Flow - Russell's current workflow for processing LLRGB images. According to Russell, "There are two guiding principles that to me determine how I proceed with the data. The first is that the signal-to-noise ratio (SNR) in the data must be meticulously preserved at every processing step. It is extremely easy to perform a processing step in such a way that noise is actually introduced into the data. You worked very hard to acquire your image data... maximize its potential."

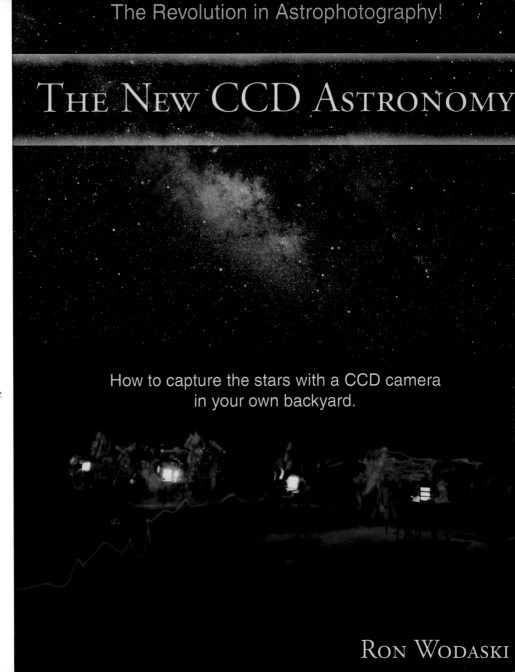

Get the book that started the revolution!

Ron Wodaski's book, *The New CCD Astronomy*, is the bible of CCD imaging. It covers everything from choosing equipment to setting it up correctly, tuning your setup to get the best results, working with color, and more.

The book also describes how to use readily available software programs like MaxIm DL and CCDSoft for both camera control and image processing.

You can order a copy of the book from your favorite astronomy retailer or online store. You can also order the book direct from the publisher's web site at:

http://www.newastro.com/newastro/order.asp

In addition to the book, you can get access to the book web site, which includes a complete online version of the book, numerous tutorials, free downloads, and more. Here is a list of chapters:

1: Using a CCD Camera
2: Practical Focusing
3: Practical Imaging
4: The Hardware Explained
5: Taking Guided Exposures
6: Increasing Image Quality
7: Color Imaging
8: Image Processing Fundamentals
9: Image Processing for Celestial Objects

The Revolution in Astrophotography!

THE NEW CCD ASTRONOMY

How to capture the stars with a CCD camera in your own backyard.

RON WODASKI

It's a secret now, but...

...we have something exciting planned. At the time of printing, we were just beginning to create an online astronomy resource that you will want to visit. We can't reveal anything specific yet (the work is being done after the book goes to the printer), but we can give you a place to look!

It should be ready by the time the book is out, or shortly thereafter.

www.NewAstroMag.com